SCIENCE: Method and Meaning

SCIENCE: Method and Meaning

EDITED BY

Samuel Rapport AND *Helen Wright*

ACADEMIC EDITORIAL ADVISER

GEORGE M. MURPHY

*Associate Dean of Arts and Science and Professor
of Chemistry, New York University*

NEW YORK UNIVERSITY PRESS 1963

© 1963 by New York University
Library of Congress Catalog Card Number: 62–17997
Manufactured in the United States of America
Designed by Andor Braun

ACKNOWLEDGMENTS

"The Method of Scientific Investigation" by T. H. Huxley, from *Darwiniana*.

"The Imperfections of Science" by Warren Weaver, from the *Proceedings of the American Philosophical Society*. Reprinted by permission of the American Philosophical Society and the author.

"In the Name of Science" from *Fads and Fallacies* by Martin Gardner. Copyright © 1952, 1957, by Martin Gardner. Reprinted by permission of Dover Publications, Inc.

"How Agassiz Taught Me to See" from *The Autobiography of Nathaniel Southgate Shaler*. Copyright 1909, by Sophia P. Shaler. Reprinted by permission of the author's estate.

"The Courtship of the Scorpion" from *The Life of the Scorpion* by J. Henri Fabre. Copyright 1923 by Dodd, Mead & Company. Reprinted by permission of Dodd, Mead & Company and Christy and Moore, Ltd.

"Mysterious Craters of the Carolina Coast" by Douglas Johnson, from *Science in Progress*, Second Series, edited by George A. Baitsell. Copyright 1940 by Yale University Press, and reprinted by permission of the Press.

"Hypothesis" from *The Art of Scientific Investigation* by W. I. B. Beveridge. All rights reserved. First published in the United States, 1950. Revised edition, 1957. Reprinted by permission of W. W. Norton & Company, Inc. and Heinemann Educational Books, Ltd.

"The Overthrow of the Phlogiston Theory" from *On Understanding Science* by James B. Conant. Copyright 1947 by Yale University Press, and reprinted by permission of the Press.

"Examples of Experimental Physiological Investigation" from *Introduction to the Study of Experimental Medicine* by Claude Bernard, translated by Henry Copley Greene.

"Chance" from *The Art of Scientific Investigation* by W. I. B. Beveridge. All rights reserved. First published in the United States, 1950. Revised edition, 1957. Reprinted by permission of W. W. Norton & Company, Inc. and Heinemann Educational Books, Ltd.

"Chain Discoveries" from *Reason and Chance in Scientific Discovery* by René Taton. Reprinted by permission of the Hutchinson Publishing Group.

"The Act of Discovery" from *The Scientific Life* by John R. Baker. Reprinted by permission of George Allen and Unwin Ltd.

"Imagination Creatrix" from *The Road to Xanadu* by John Livingston Lowes. Copyright 1927 by John Livingston Lowes. Reprinted by permission of and arrangement with Houghton Mifflin Company, the authorized publishers.

"The Night Prowler" by Otto Loewi, from *Perspectives in Biology and Medicine* (1960). Copyright 1961 by the University of Chicago. Reprinted by permission of the University of Chicago Press.

"The Miracle That Saved the World" from *Men and Atoms* by William L. Laurence. Copyright © 1946, 1959, 1962 by William L. Laurence. Reprinted by permission of Simon and Schuster, Inc. and Hodder and Stoughton, Limited.

"The Fourth Adjustment" from *Of Stars and Men* by Harlow Shapley. Copyright © 1958 by Harlow Shapley. Reprinted by permission of Beacon Press and Elek Books, Ltd.

"Science and the Education of Free Men" by Edmund W. Sinnott, from *The American Scientist,* July, 1944. Copyright © by the Society of the Sigma Xi. Reprinted by permission of the author.

"Science and Sensibility" from *The Common Sense of Science* by J. Bronowski. Reprinted by permission of Harvard University Press and William Heinemann, Ltd.

"A Scientific Society—the Beginnings" by Glenn T. Seaborg. Reprinted by permission of the author.

"Science as a Means of International Understanding" from *Philosophical Problems in Nuclear Science* by Werner Karl Heisenberg. Copyright 1952 by Pantheon Books, Inc. Reprinted by permission of Pantheon Books, Inc. and Faber and Faber, Ltd.

"Religion and Science" reprinted with permission of the publisher from *Science and the Modern World* by Alfred North Whitehead. Copyright, 1925 by the Macmillan Company. Copyright, 1953, by Evelyn Whitehead.

The E. E. Cummings poetry quoted on page 16 is reprinted with permission of the author and Harcourt, Brace & World, Inc.

CONTENTS

II. Science and the World Around Us

FOREWORD

THIS BOOK, containing excerpts from the writings of distinguished scientists, should be fascinating to the nontechnical reader. There are no forbidding mathematical equations here, nor are there any austere graphs. The words and punctuation are the same as those found in the daily newspaper. The only difference is in the subject matter. Instead of local or international affairs, dramatic or musical criticism, sports or other matters of contemporary interest, the ideas of concern here are the scientific method and the relation of science to the world in which we live.

Most elementary science textbooks contain a few sentences or many paragraphs on the scientific method. This method differs, to some extent at least, from the methods used in history, economics, musicology, or other subjects commonly called the humanities. There is no better way to understand it than to read about it in the scientists' own words. There are no dull dictionary definitions here but exciting examples of ways in which science proceeds.

The natural sciences, of course, are experimental, and the first step of the scientist is always a record of an observed fact in nature or the laboratory. The observations lead, in turn, to hypotheses, theories, and laws. It must be expected that every theory will suggest some new experiment which should be done, and it might be hoped that the result will disagree with the theory, at least in some way. The theory is then modified to explain the newly observed fact, a new experiment is performed, and thus science develops. It would be an uninteresting subject indeed if the theories were so perfect that they explained all known facts.

Some years ago, the scientist was generally regarded as a strange individual who performed peculiar operations in a laboratory. The same opinion may still be held by many, but today the scientist cannot isolate himself from the world nor can the nonscientist avoid trying to understand him. As never before in history, the scientist must explain himself to the society in which he lives and relate himself to the intellectual achievements of those who reach conclusions by other methods. If this book can help in these ways, its purpose has been served.

George M. Murphy

INTRODUCTION

THE IMPORTANCE OF SCIENCE in our daily lives has been so thoroughly recognized that it need hardly be restated. It has revolutionized warfare, manufacture, agriculture, communication, mining, and almost every other activity with which man busies himself. It is hardly possible to prepare a general book on science without referring to these contributions. But, while numerous applications of science are mentioned in the following pages, they occur merely as by-products of a larger thesis. This thesis is the fundamental meaning of science—what it consists of, how its practitioners operate, and how it affects the concepts of educated men.

Perhaps the most important revelation of recent years has been the desperate need for an understanding of these aspects of science and the general public's almost total ignorance of them. Nor is this ignorance limited to the man in the street. It extends into the highest reaches of business, finance, and government. A secretary of war who had been president of the world's largest manufacturing corporation was quoted as defining fundamental research as "when you don't know what you are doing." Given an acceptance of this idea by those in power, a civilization will decline as inevitably as if it were devastated by atomic bombs. On October 4th, 1957, the Russians launched into orbit an object which added the word "sputnik" to our vocabulary. Immediately there was an unprecedented furor. Fear that the West was being outstripped in technological advances led to a re-examination of our scientific education and research. What was, and perhaps continues to be, insufficiently understood was the exact direction these activities should take. Even the most far-reaching applications—the steam engine, the electric power plant, the atomic bomb, the interplanetary rocket—are the result of those activities in which "you don't know what you are doing."

But basic science has values other than practical applications. It has profound things to say about mankind's loftiest aspirations—his search for truth, beauty, and goodness. In this book, as well as in the other volumes in THE NEW YORK UNIVERSITY LIBRARY OF SCIENCE, some of the greatest scientists and philosophers tell what they have learned about these aspirations. A volume of this size, dealing with a subject so vast, must necessarily be limited in subject matter. Some of the selections have been included in abbreviated form, and, as the book is addressed primarily to the educated layman, scholarly apparatus has been omitted. It is hoped that it will entice the reader into further investigation.

SCIENCE: METHOD AND MEANING is one of the books in the series entitled THE NEW YORK UNIVERSITY LIBRARY OF SCIENCE. Other volumes, dealing with individual sciences, are either published or in preparation. The series as a whole will encompass much of the universe of modern man, for that universe has been shaped in greatest measure by science, the branch of human activity whose name is derived from the Latin *scire*—to know.

I. SCIENCE and the Scientist

A. The Nature of Scientific Activity

B. Observation, Hypothesis, Experiment

C. Discovery

I. Science and the Scientist

A. The Nature of Scientific Activity

The following selection is considered one of the classic statements of what science is. Originally addressed to an audience of British workingmen, it explains the meanings of induction, deduction, and hypothesis, words that are often frightening to the uninitiated, in everyday terms. This was science as it was understood in the nineteenth century. Even today it is used by many teachers as an introduction to the methodology of science. In its clarity and persuasiveness we see the qualities that made Huxley one of the foremost interpreters of science. And if, as we shall see, it lacks the sophistication that contemporary scientific thinking demands, it remains an ideal basic description.

Thomas Henry Huxley was born in Ealing, near London, in 1825. Although the son of a schoolmaster, he received little formal education. He managed to overcome this handicap to become in turn a physician and a biologist. The submission of one of his biology papers to the Royal Society resulted in his election as a Fellow in 1851, and he received the Royal Society's medal when only twenty-six. His creative work has been dwarfed by his skill as a polemicist. At a time when science, and particularly Darwinism, was under the bitterest attack, he was largely responsible for the defeat of reaction and the acceptance of the new scientific ideas. He was also the nineteenth century's leading exponent of scientific education. To him, more than to any other individual, may be credited the emphasis on physical and biological science in the curricula of Great Britain and, by osmosis, of the United States.

THE METHOD OF SCIENTIFIC INVESTIGATION

T. H. HUXLEY

THE METHOD of scientific investigation is nothing but the expression of the necessary mode of working of the human mind. It is simply the mode at which all phenomena are reasoned about, rendered precise and exact. There is no more difference, but there is just the same kind of difference, between the mental operations of a man of science and those of an ordinary person, as there is between the operations and methods of a baker or of a butcher weighing out his goods in common scales, and the operations of a chemist in performing a difficult and complex analysis by means of his balance and finely graduated scales. It is not that the action of the scales in the one case, and the balance in the other, differ in the principles of their construction or manner of working; but the beam of one is set on an infinitely finer axis than the other, and of course turns by the addition of a much smaller weight.

You will understand this better, perhaps, if I give you some familiar example. You have all heard it repeated, I dare say, that men of science work by means of induction and deduction, and that by the help of these operations, they, in a sort of sense, wring from Nature certain other things, which are called natural laws, and causes, and that out of these, by some cunning skill of their own, they build up hypotheses and theories. And it is imagined by many, that the operations of the common mind can be by no means compared with these processes, and that they have to be acquired by a sort of special apprenticeship to the craft. To hear all these large words, you would think that the mind of a man of science must be constituted differently from that of his fellow men; but if you will not be frightened by terms, you will discover that you are quite wrong, and that all these terrible apparatus are being used by yourselves every day and every hour of your lives.

There is a well-known incident in one of Molière's plays,[1] where the author makes the hero express unbounded delight on being told that he had been talking prose during the whole of his life. In the same way, I trust, that you will take comfort, and be delighted with yourselves, on the discovery that you have been acting on the principles of inductive and deductive philosophy during the same period. Probably there is not one here who has not in the course of the day had occasion to set in motion a complex train of reasoning, of the very same kind, though differing of course in degree, as that which a scientific man goes through in tracing the causes of natural phenomena.

A very trivial circumstance will serve to exemplify this. Suppose you go into a fruiterer's shop, wanting an apple— you take up one, and, on biting it, you find it is sour; you look at it, and see that it is hard and green. You take up another one, and that too is hard, green, and sour. The shopman offers you a third; but, before biting it, you examine it, and find that it is hard and green, and you immediately say that you will not have it, as it must be sour, like those that you have already tried.

Nothing can be more simple than that, you think; but if you will take the trouble to analyze and trace out into its logical elements what has been done by the mind, you will be greatly surprised. In the first place, you have performed the operation of induction. You found that, in two experiences, hardness and greenness in apples went together with sourness. It was so in the first case, and it was confirmed by the second. True, it is a very small basis, but still it is enough to make an induction from; you generalize the facts, and you expect to find sourness in apples where you get hardness and greenness. You found upon that a general law, that all hard and green apples are sour; and that, so far as it goes, is a perfect induction. Well, having got your natural law in this way, when you are offered another apple which you find is hard and green, you say, "All hard

1. Le Bourgeois Gentilhomme.

and green apples are sour; this apple is hard and green, therefore this apple is sour." That train of reasoning is what logicians call a syllogism, and has all its various parts and terms—its major premise, its minor premise, and its conclusion, and, by the help of further reasoning, which, if drawn out, would have to be exhibited in two or three other syllogisms, you arrive at your final determination, "I will not have that apple." So that, you see, you have, in the first place, established a law by induction, and upon that you have founded a deduction, and reasoned out the special conclusion of the particular case. Well now, suppose, having got your law, that at some time afterwards, you are discussing the qualities of apples with a friend: you will say to him, "It is a very curious thing—but I find that all hard and green apples are sour!" Your friend says to you, "But how do you know that?" You at once reply, "Oh, because I have tried them over and over again, and have always found them to be so." Well, if we were talking science instead of common sense, we should call that an experimental verification. And, if still opposed, you go further, and say, "I have heard from the people of Somersetshire and Devonshire, where a large number of apples are grown, that they have observed the same thing. It is also found to be the case in Normandy, and in North America. In short, I find it to be the universal experience of mankind wherever attention has been directed to the subject." Whereupon, your friend, unless he is a very unreasonable man, agrees with you, and is convinced that you are quite right in the conclusion you have drawn. He believes, although perhaps he does not know he believes it, that the more extensive verifications are—that the more frequently experiments have been made, and results of the same kind arrived at—that the more varied the conditions under which the same results are obtained the more certain is the ultimate conclusion, and he disputes the question no further. He sees that the experiment has been tried under all sorts of conditions, as to time, place, and people, with the same result; and he says with you, therefore, that the law you have laid down must be a good one, and he must believe it.

In science we do the same thing—the philosopher exercises precisely the same faculties, though in a much more delicate manner. In scientific inquiry it becomes a matter of duty to expose a supposed law to every possible kind of verification, and to take care, moreover, that this is done intentionally, and not left to a mere accident, as in the case of the apples. And in science, as in common life, our confidence in a law is in exact proportion to the absence of variation in the result of our experimental verifications. For instance, if you let go your grasp of an article you may have in your hand, it will immediately fall to the ground. That is a very common verification of one of the best established laws of nature—that of gravitation. The method by which men of science establish the existence of that law is exactly the same as that by which we have established the trivial proposition about the sourness of hard and green apples. But we believe it in such an extensive, thorough, and unhesitating manner because the universal experience of mankind verifies it, and we can verify it ourselves at any time; and that is the strongest possible foundation on which any natural law can rest.

So much, then, by way of proof that the method of establishing laws in science is exactly the same as that pursued in common life. Let us now turn to another matter (though really it is but another phase of the same question), and that it, the method by which, from the relations of certain phenomena, we prove that some stand in the position of causes towards the others.

I want to put the case clearly before you, and will therefore show you what I mean by another familiar example. I will suppose that one of you, on coming down in the morning to the parlor of your house, finds that a tea-pot and some spoons which had been left in the room on the previous evening are gone—the window is open, and you observe the mark of a dirty hand on the window-frame, and perhaps, in addition to that, you notice the impress of a hobnailed shoe on the gravel outside. All these phenomena have struck your attention instantly, and before two seconds have passed you say, "Oh, somebody has broken open the window, entered the room, and run off with the spoons and the tea-pot!" That speech is out of your mouth in a moment. And you will probably add, "I know there has; I am quite sure of it!" You mean to say exactly what you know; but in reality you are giving expression to what is, in all essential particulars, an hypothesis. You do not *know* it at all; it is nothing but an hypothesis rapidly framed in our own mind. And it is an hypothesis founded on a long train of inductions and deductions.

What are those inductions and deductions, and how have you got at this hypothesis? You have observed, in the first place, that the window is open; but by a train of reasoning involving many inductions and deductions, you have probably arrived long before at the general law—and a very good one it is—that windows do not open of themselves; and you therefore conclude that something has opened the window. A second general law that you have arrived at in the same way is, that teapots and spoons do not go out of a window spontaneously, and you are satisfied that, as they are not now where you left them, they have been removed. In the third place, you look at the marks on the window-sill, and the shoe-marks outside, and you say that in all previous experience the former kind of mark had never been produced by anything else but the hand of a human being; and the same experience shows that no other animal but man at present wears shoes with hob-nails in them such as would produce the marks in the gravel. I do not know, even if we could discover any of those "missing links" that are talked about, that they would help us to any other conclusion! At any rate the law which states our present experience is strong enough for my present purpose. You next reach the conclusion that, as these kinds of marks have not been left by any other animal than man, or are liable to be formed in any other way than by a man's hand and shoe, the marks in question have been formed by a man in that way. You have, further, a general law, founded on observation and experience, and that, too, is, I am sorry to say, a very universal and unimpeachable one—that some men are thieves; and you assume at once from all these premises

—and that is what constitutes your hypothesis—that the man who made the marks outside and on the window-sill, opened the window, got into the room, and stole your teapot and spoons. You have now arrived at a *vera causa*—you have assumed a cause which, it is plain, is competent to produce all the phenomena you have observed. You can explain all these phenomena only by the hypothesis of a thief. But that is an hypothetical conclusion, of the justice of which you have no absolute proof at all; it is only rendered highly probable by a series of inductive and deductive reasonings.

I suppose your first action, assuming that you are a man of ordinary common sense, and that you have established this hypothesis to your own satisfaction, will very likely be to go off for the police, and set them on the track of the burglar, with the view to the recovery of your property. But just as you are starting with this object, some person comes in, and on learning what you are about, says, "My good friend, you are going on a great deal too fast. How do you know that the man who really made the marks took the spoons? It might have been a monkey that took them, and the man may have merely looked in afterwards." You would probably reply, "Well, that is all very well, but you see it is contrary to all experience of the way teapots and spoons are abstracted; so that, at any rate, your hypothesis is less probable than mine." While you are talking the thing over in this way, another friend arrives, one of the good kind of people that I was talking of a little while ago. And he might say, "Oh, my dear sir, you are certainly going on a great deal too fast. You are most presumptuous. You admit that all these occurrences took place when you were fast asleep, at a time when you could not possibly have known anything about what was taking place. How do you know that the laws of Nature are not suspended during the night? It may be that there has been some kind of supernatural interference in this case." In point of fact, he declares that your hypothesis is one of which you cannot at all demonstrate the truth, and that you are by no means sure that the laws of Nature are the same when you are asleep as when you are awake.

Well, now, you cannot at the moment answer that kind of reasoning. You feel that your worthy friend has you somewhat at a disadvantage. You will feel perfectly convinced in your own mind, however, that you are quite right, and you say to him, "My good friend, I can only be guided by the natural probabilities of the case, and if you will be kind enough to stand aside and permit me to pass, I will go and fetch the police." Well, we will suppose that your journey is successful, and that by good luck you meet with a policeman; that eventually the burglar is found with your property on his person, and the marks correspond to his hand and to his boots. Probably any jury would consider those facts a very good experimental verification of your hypothesis, touching the cause of the abnormal phenomena observed in your parlor, and would act accordingly.

Now, in this supposititious case, I have taken phenomena of a very common kind, in order that you might see what are the different steps in an ordinary process of reasoning, if you will only take the trouble to analyze it carefully. All the operations I have described, you will see, are involved in the mind of any man of sense in leading him to a conclusion as to the course he should take in order to make good a robbery and punish the offender. I say that you are led, in that case, to your conclusion by exactly the same train of reasoning as that which a man of science pursues when he is endeavoring to discover the origin and laws of the most occult phenomena. The process is, and always must be, the same; and precisely the same mode of reasoning was employed by Newton and Laplace in their endeavors to discover and define the causes of the movements of the heavenly bodies, as you, with your own common sense, would employ to detect a burglar. The only difference is, that the nature of the inquiry being more abstruse, every step has to be most carefully watched, so that there may not be a single crack or flaw in your hypothesis. A flaw or crack in many of the hypotheses of daily life may be of little or no moment as affecting the general correctness of the conclusions at which we may arrive; but, in a scientific inquiry, a fallacy, great or small, is always of importance, and is sure to be in the long run constantly productive of mischievous, if not fatal results.

Do not allow yourselves to be misled by the common notion that an hypothesis is untrustworthy simply because it is an hypothesis. It is often urged, in respect to some scientific conclusion that, after all, it is only an hypothesis. But what more have we to guide us in nine-tenths of the most important affairs of daily life than hypotheses, and often very ill-based ones? So that in science, where the evidence of an hypothesis is subjected to the most rigid examination, we may rightly pursue the same course. You may have hypotheses and hypotheses. A man may say, if he likes, that the moon is made of green cheese: that is an hypothesis. But another man, who has devoted a great deal of time and attention to the subject, and availed himself of the powerful telescopes and the results of the observations of others, declares that in his opinion it is probably composed of materials very similar to those of which our own earth is made up: and that is also only an hypothesis. But I need not tell you that there is an enormous difference in the value of the two hypotheses. That one which is based on sound scientific knowledge is sure to have a corresponding value; and that which is a mere hasty random guess is likely to have but little value. Every great step in our progress in discovering causes has been made in exactly the same way as that which I have detailed to you. A person observing the occurrence of certain facts and phenomena asks, naturally enough, what process, what kind of operation known to occur in Nature, applied to the particular case, will unravel and explain the mystery? Hence you have the scientific hypothesis; and its value will be proportionate to the care and completeness with which its basis had been tested and verified. It is in these matters as in the commonest affairs of practical life: the guess of the fool will be folly, while the guess of the wise man will contain wisdom. In all cases, you see that the value of the result depends on the patience and faithfulness with which the investigator applies to his hypothesis every possible kind of verification.

Wherever there are complex masses of phenomena to be inquired into, whether they be phenomena of the affairs of daily life, or whether they belong to the more abstruse and difficult problems laid before the philosopher, our course of proceeding in unravelling that complex chain of phenomena with a view to get at its cause, is always the same; in all cases we must invent an hypothesis; we must place before ourselves some more or less likely supposition respecting that cause; and then, having assumed an hypothesis, having supposed a cause for the phenomena in question, we must endeavor, on the one hand, to demonstrate our hypothesis, or, on the other, to upset and reject it altogether, by testing it in three ways. We must, in the first place, be prepared to prove that the supposed causes of the phenomena exist in nature; that they are what the logicians call *verae causae*— true causes; in the next place, we should be prepared to show that the assumed causes of the phenomena are competent to produce such as those we wish to explain by them; and in the last place, we ought to be able to show that no other known causes are competent to produce these phenomena. If we can succeed in satisfying these three conditions, we shall have demonstrated our hypothesis; or rather I ought to say, we shall have proved it as far as certainty is possible for us; for, after all, there is no one of our surest convictions which may not be upset, or at any rate modified by a further accession of knowledge. It was because it satisfied these conditions that we accepted the hypothesis as to the disappearance of the tea-pot and spoons in the case I supposed; we found that our hypothesis on that subject was tenable and valid, because the supposed cause existed in nature, because it was competent to account for the phenomena, and because no other known cause was competent to account for them; and it is upon similar grounds that any hypothesis you choose to name is accepted in science as tenable and valid.

Dr. Weaver's article is the logical contemporary outgrowth of Huxley's nineteenth-century point of view. He shows how exceedingly complex modern science has become and how in many areas, particularly those of the extremely small or the extremely large, the common-sense approach has little validity. Science is not perfect, because it is the creation of human beings who are themselves imperfect. It offers no absolute knowledge, no ultimate answers, and no complete fulfillment of human needs and desires. Such limitations have often been used in attacks on the fundamental value of science and in the furtherance of ignorance and bigotry. As Dr. Weaver who has been one of the leaders in counteracting this viewpoint explains, the edifice of science is powerful enough to acknowledge the limitations and withstand the attacks.

Warren Weaver was born in Wisconsin in 1894 and became a professor of mathematics at the University of Wisconsin in 1920. In 1932 he was appointed Director of the Division of Natural Sciences of the Rockefeller Foundation, and in 1955 Vice-President for the Natural and Medical Sciences. He is now Vice-President of the Alfred P. Sloan Foundation. In these positions he has had great influence on scientific progress in the United States.

THE IMPERFECTIONS OF SCIENCE

WARREN WEAVER

AS MY TITLE INDICATES, I am going to be speaking of imperfections; but I must warn you that I will also be speaking of something which I love. My text is, therefore, almost inevitable:

My mistress' eyes are nothing like the sun;
Coral is far more red than her lips' red:
If snow be white, why then her breasts are dun;
If hairs be wires, black wires grow on her head.

I have seen roses damask'd, red and white,
But no such roses see I in her cheeks;
And in some perfumes is there more delight
Than in the breath that from my mistress reeks.
I love to hear her speak, yet well I know
That music hath a far more pleasant sound.
I grant I never saw a goddess go,
My mistress, when she walks, treads on the ground.
  And yet, by heaven, I think my love as rare
  As any she belied with false compare.

Yes, if I were going to over-load this talk with a sub-title, it would have to be "The Dark Lady of the Laboratories."

I propose to consider two questions. First, why does science command the respect, prestige, and admiration which it obviously possesses? Second, does science really deserve the reputation which is often, if not usually, given to it by scientists and public alike: and is it not possible to take a more restrained, more candid, and, I believe, more accurate attitude toward science which honestly concedes certain limitations, while still permitting one to declaim "And yet, by heaven, I think my love as rare. . . ."

It may seem surprising, and even trivial, to ask why science has so great a reputation. We are, in the modern world, completely surrounded by science and by the technological achievements which science makes possible. By this powerful partnership we are warmed and cooled, clothed and fed, protected, cured, transported, and entertained. Science has made possible color television and jets, dial telephones across the continent and short-wave radio across the oceans, polio serum, hi-fi and stereo, heart, lung and kidney-function machines which substitute temporarily for our own damaged internal parts, electronic computers that play chess and compose music, satellites about the earth and rockets to the moon, automatization and microminiaturization, machines that think and which learn from experience (which is more than some people do), nuclear energy, and G. L. 76 in toothpaste. If we have not yet conquered cancer, cardiac disorders, and the degenerative diseases of later life; if we are uncertain about the genetic effects of long continued low doses of radiation; if we miss recovering a nose-cone now and then; if we are a little puzzled about psychology and psychiatry and are not yet sure whether the mind is in the head; if we still have cavities in our teeth, aches in our joints, and clocks that won't run in our automobiles—well, surely these are minor gaps which will soon be filled in by science.

Indeed, there is a good deal of evidence that if science once chooses to drive a path out into the wilderness of ignorance, then, no matter where that path is headed, there seems to be no inherent limitation to the distance science can penetrate, no limit to the amount of experience that can be explained and brought under control by the methods of science. These continuing successes have been convincing enough in the field of the physical sciences—in astronomy and chemistry and physics, for example. In our modern physical laboratories we transmute the elements, and change mass to energy and *vice versa*. We experiment with fantastic entities ludicrously called elementary particles—the most evanescent of which exist for less than one-hundred-thousandth of a billionth of a second. The high polymer chemist has become a skilled atomic architect, using atoms to build molecules of which nature never thought, synthesizing a whole array of new materials of great beauty and utility, each built to blueprint specifications concerning the desired strength, density, color, thermal and electric properties, resistance to wear, or stain, or corrosion, etc. We create an electrical disturbance in the recently discovered radiation belt thousands of miles above the surface of our earth; and, sure enough, auroral lights appear at another and far distant location on our planet, just at the time theoretically predicted.

Yes, the triumphs of the physical scientists are impressive enough to explain why science has a great reputation. But the triumphs of those parts of science which are concerned with living nature are, in many ways, to be interpreted even more seriously. For it seems, on the whole, reasonable and proper for man to analyze his physical environment.

But the mysteries of life—perhaps they are intended to *remain* mysteries.

Therefore the reputation of science becomes even greater, even more formidable, perhaps even more disturbing, when one success after another seems to indicate that many central and precious vital phenomena will one day be explainable in terms of chemistry and physics, that the very stuff of life will one day be weighed and measured and put on the shelf in neatly labeled bottles.

The age-long history of man's learning about plants and about the lower animals contributed to the good reputation of science without creating any large counter-feeling of apprehension. But when the first brave anatomists invaded the human body, and the early physiologists began to analyze man's own parts in mechanical terms, then the philosophers and humanists and theologians were convinced that they could hear the distant footsteps of an all-conquering science monster.

The great Darwinian movement, whose centennial we have so recently celebrated, has seemed to many to constitute the major indication that man, if he is indeed nothing but an improved beast, can by one more easy step be nothing more than a mere machine—and thus surely an object which science can wholly analyze, wholly capture within its special framework.

When experiments show that the normal mothering behavior of an animal—the concern to feed and clean and protect the very young offspring—is destroyed by leaving a metallic trace element out of the diet; when the modern biochemist can explore inside the mitochondria within a cell and analyze the enzyme systems there; when the microbiologist can take a virus apart into chemically identifiable and wholly "dead" pieces and then can reconstitute these pieces into an organism which can reproduce itself—then indeed science begins to earn a reputation which is in many senses great, but which is also in some senses frightening.

Modern advances in genetics, and especially in the fundamental biochemical aspects of genetic phenomena, may well be the greatest and most spectacular, as well as the most formidable, triumph of science in its attack on the living world. It is convincing enough—and fearsome enough—when the physicist learns to control the energy in the nuclei of atoms. But what will we think of science, and how will we order our lives, when the biologist has learned how to control the gene? This will clearly present the greatest intellectual and moral challenge that man has ever faced.

So science has never really been blocked, it seems, no matter in what direction it seeks to move.

So science has, it seems, been so successful that it has inevitably earned a great and strange reputation. If it has never yet been defeated, presumably it is all-powerful. And since science is, after all, the work of scientists—for one seldom encounters disembodied science—then presumably these scientists are both so clever and so wise that *they* can do anything. Perhaps we should turn the world over to this superbreed. Perhaps they could, if properly supported, really liberated, and put in charge—perhaps they could solve all problems of human relations, of economic stability, of international peace, and of the good life. Perhaps they should design not only the churches, but the creeds also. Perhaps the best music and the loveliest poetry *will*, in a short time, come out of a machine.

The sad fact is that some scientists themselves appear to believe precisely this. And this arrogant attitude quite naturally irritates, or even angers, the social scientists, the humanists, the moralists, and the creative artists. The classic protest is surely that of Keats.

> *Do not all charms fly*
> *At the mere touch of cold philosophy?*
> *There was an awful rainbow once in Heaven:*
> *We know her woof, her textures; she is given*
> *In the dull catalogue of common things.*
> *Philosophy will clip an Angel's wings.*

In more contemporary terms, and at the same time that the electronics engineer is programming his computer to write verse, the modern poet E. E. Cummings writes

I'd rather learn from one bird how to sing
than teach ten thousand stars how not to dance.

or, in still more-up-to-date idiom,

(While you and i have lips and voices which
are for kissing and to sing with
who cares if some oneeyed son of a bitch
invents an instrument to measure Spring with?

Our first question is thus answered. Science has its remarkable reputation primarily because of its record of success in dealing with inanimate nature—with the physical
universe—and secondarily because of the promising advances it has already made in understanding and controlling
vital phenomena. These have brought to science a great
prestige and respect. Often this prestige and respect rest
upon quite the wrong evidence—on relatively trivial matters,
or on advances which are essentially technological rather
than basically scientific in character. And these successes
have, while earning admiration from some, aroused resentment and fear and opposition in others. Worst of all, these
successes have tended to separate scientists out as a special
breed, and have widened, rather than narrowed, the gap
between scientific thought and general learning.

To advance to our second question, does science deserve
either the favorable or the unfavorable parts of its reputation? Can science not be given a more true, more realistic,
and more constructive interpretation?

I think that the favorable part of the present reputation
of science is often significantly misunderstood; and I think
that the unfavorable part is largely if not wholly false. And
in explaining why, I shall at the same time be giving my
personal answer to the other aspect of our second question;
namely, is there not a more balanced view of science which
puts both its power and its limitations into a more clear and
more correct focus?

To deal with these questions we must start with pretty
basic considerations. When man—scientific man—confronts

any object, any natural phenomenon, what does he wish to do? He does not elect to disregard, he dislikes being mystified, he is not willing to fear. On the contrary, he has a deep craving to *understand*. The difference between the state of *not understanding* and of *understanding* is a complex and subtle matter which has several aspects, of differing importance to different persons. It seems best to start by describing what aspects of understanding are of major importance to a scientist. We do not have time to consider the way in which the scientific view on this point has changed, as science has developed; nor do we have time to describe the differing views that are held by scientists even today. I shall state only a view which is held by a good many experts, particularly among the quantum theorists, this being incidentally the view which, with certain modification, I myself find congenial.

For a scientist, a phenomenon is *understood* provided he possesses a satisfactory *theory* for this phenomenon. But this statement is not very illuminating until one goes on to say what a satisfactory scientific theory is, how it operates, and in what senses it is useful or interesting or both.

The theory, in refined cases and in the physical sciences, is likely to consist of a body of mathematical equations. These equations state the interdependence of a few or several quantities, represented simply by letters in the equations. If you point to one of the letters and ask, "What is this: what physical thing does this represent?" then the answer, at least from the group here being described, is that you have asked an irrelevant and improper question.

For associated with this body of equations is a set of procedural rules. You are told: "Perform such and such observations, either in a laboratory experiment set up thus and so, or directly upon nature in such and such a way. Take the numbers which result from those observations, and put them into these equations, substituting the numbers for certain specified letters. Then solve the equations, thus obtaining numerical values for certain other letters. Now go back to your experiment (or another similar one), or go back to nature and make certain further observations. This

will provide you with a new set of numbers: and if you
have a sound theory, these new numbers will coincide (with
certain probabilistic error which need not confuse us at the
moment) with the numbers which were previously solved
out of the equations."

Now I am fully aware of your disappointment over this
statement. It sounds very formal and abstract—and it is.
The procedure sounds complicated—and often it is in fact
exceedingly complicated. And how can this procedure possibly bring about *understanding?*

Let us, therefore, drop this line of attack for a moment,
and consider a more friendly, more understandable sort of
understanding. A person says, "I don't understand genetics
at all. I don't understand genes and chromosomes." He is
told, "Well, a chromosome (in every cell of your body, incidentally) is sort of like a string of beads, each bead being
a gene. And each gene determines, or helps to determine,
one of your characteristics, such as your blue eyes, or your
attached earlobes, or, for that matter, your sex." And the
person thinks, "Well, this is something like it; I am beginning
to understand."

Or this same eager person says, "I don't understand radio
waves." And he is told, "Well, throw a small stone into a still
pond of water. See those circular ripples expand, getting
weaker as they go? See the *wave length,* which is merely
the distance from the crest of one ripple to the crest of the
adjacent ripple? See how these waves would *keep* expanding out, if you kept throwing little stones in at the same
spot? Well, radio waves are like that, although of course
they are three-dimensional spherical ripples." And again
the person thinks, "I am beginning to understand."

With these extreme examples before us—of a very abstract
and formal theory on the one hand, and of a friendly, loose,
incomplete, but nevertheless useful analogy on the other
hand, we can now contrast two extreme concepts of understanding.

One of these, the friendly, man-in-the-street variety, attempts to explain by describing an unfamiliar phenomenon
in terms of its similarity to a familiar phenomenon. The fact

that this kind of explanation by analogy is comforting, that it satisfies the listener, is, if you stop to think about it, rather surprising. For logically and philosophically this procedure is a complete fraud. The unfamiliar is explained in terms of the familiar. But the *familiar,* if one examines the situation honestly and in detail, is itself simply *not understood.* It has been familiar long enough so that curiosity concerning it has disappeared; but that is all.

Although referred to here as the "man-in-the-street" type of explanation, it should be pointed out that scientists are often found in this same street. Science very frequently uses this form of explanation, and it has to recommend it not only the fact that it is comforting, but also the fact that it is useful. For if radio waves are "like" water waves or more generally like waves in other familiar media, then to the new and strange phenomena of radio can at once be applied a lot of the previously accumulated knowledge about more familiar waves.

The other, formal, type of procedure is, again, clearly *not an explanation,* in any normal sense of that word. In fact it baldly states that the scientist has no business to ask, "What is the real nature of physical phenomena"; or to ask, "Are there really precise deterministic laws behind the statistical data which I observe"; or to ask, "How *can* light be both a wave motion and a beam of particles"; or to ask, "What sense does it make for a particle to have electric charge but zero mass?"

These are, to the one who accepts the formal procedure, senseless assortments of words. For the formal procedure makes no pretense whatsoever of "explaining." The formal procedure, in fact, says "It is impossible to explain phenomena, and it is in fact senseless to try. All you can do—and this is a triumph of great dimensions—is to *deal successfully* with phenomena."

The equations, or more generally the theory, are a sort of "black box." You can feed one set of numbers into this black box, turn the crank, and out comes a second set of numbers. If this second set correlates properly with numbers which can be determined, following given rules, from nature, then you have a successful theory. You must accept the result, be thankful, and ask no further questions.

This idea of *not explaining*, but of *dealing successfully* with phenomena deserves a few further words. What, to the scientists, constitutes a really satisfactory sort of success for a theory?

The answer lies largely in the words *generality, elegance, control,* and *prediction*. If one single theory—one black box —is capable of grinding out results that relate to a wide range and a large apparent diversity of experience, then the theory has the obvious practical advantage of *generality*. It is a convenient intellectual tool that will handle a lot of different jobs. And this generality also has an important aesthetic aspect, for it reveals underlying unity in apparent diversity—a procedure which the creative artist recognizes as very closely related to the concept of beauty. If in addition the theory is stated in compact form, then it possesses the illusive but lovely trait which the scientist calls "elegance."

Suppose that the black box of our theory has certain dials on one of its faces, and that we set these dials, before inserting input data, to values which are characteristic of the particular experiment in question. Then the numbers ground out by our black box will depend not only on the numbers we insert, but also on our dial settings. And then by changing these dial settings one can answer such a question as "How will the result change if I vary one or more of the circumstances of the experiment?" As more specific examples, "How will the electrical resistance of this alloy change if I put more tin in the alloy? . . . How much further can the aircraft fly if I increase the fuel capacity by 500 gallons? . . . How much faster will I lose weight if I reduce from 1,400 calories a day to 1,200 calories?" Under useful circumstances such as these, the theory has brought the phenomenon under *control*. You know just what to do in order to modify the result in the desired way.

Finally, the black box, if it is a really good one, must be able to grind out numbers which will prove to correlate properly with numbers which you will obtain in an experiment or observation *not yet made*. That is to say, the theory should be able to *predict*.

We can now state in more compact summary what the modern scientist—or at least one important school of scientists—calls a good theory. It is a small and neat black box which works for a wide range of problems, which has external dials which can be set, and which can be used in advance. In other words, it is a theory which is *general* and *elegant*, which puts us in *control* of the phenomena in question, and which can *predict*. But notice that I have not said one single word about *explaining*. The advocates of abstract theories have to agree that the scientist *understands* a phenomenon when he can *control* and *predict* it, and that as a product of his creative imagination he appreciates and admires the theory the more, the more *general* and *elegant* it is. Within the formal view here being described, nothing more by way of explanation can in the nature of things be demanded or expected.

It is essential to my general argument to point out at once that many scientists enthusiastically disagree with this position. One of the most competent and moving objections would be made by the distinguished scholar Michael Polanyi, earlier a physical chemist and now a social scientist and philosopher. Polanyi, to whose general views we will return later, considers that the abstract and formal procedures in science are, in fact, useless and senseless unless, quite in addition and as a subjective and very personal experience, the totality of the formal manipulation "makes sense." Polanyi points out that he himself has traced every successive step involved in the proof of certain theorems, but that nevertheless

They have conveyed nothing to me, for I have not been able to grasp their sequence as a whole. . . . To look at a mathematical proof by merely verifying each consecutive step—says Poincaré—is like watching a game of chess, noting only that each step obeys the rules of chess. The least that is required is a grasp of the logical sequence as a purposeful procedure: what Poincaré describes as the "something which constitutes the unity of the demonstration."

Having characterized a successful scientific theory, we can now use some of the terms of that description to restate the reasons why science has so great a standing.

Indeed, the general and popular reputation of science rests largely on its success at *control,* and to a lesser degree upon its ability to *predict.* Unfortunately, only scientists themselves, and a few others who make a real effort, achieve the knowledge that makes *generality* important, and *elegance* lovely.

When we restrict attention to moderate-scale phenomena, involving, say, objects above electron-microscopic size, and if we stay away from such phenomena as the toss of a single coin or the decisions of a single mind, then science can often offer "explanation by analogy," this being useful, interesting, and curiously comforting. But this kind of explanation is, fundamentally, a complete illusion: and at the other extreme the strict and formal abstract type of a scientific theory contains nothing whatsoever that constitutes, in any ordinary sense, explanation.

This is a rather shocking thing to say—that science does not furnish any really ultimate or satisfying explanation. And this imperfection leads at once to the question: Does science have other important imperfections?

Without claiming completeness, I want to speak here of a total of five imperfections. You will not be surprised, I think, to have me say that these are not, actually, so much imperfections in science as imperfection in the views that are held by some concerning science. To those who expect science to be perfect, who expect it to be irresistibly all-powerful, who think of it as being infinitely precise and logically impeccable, who see science marching relentlessly forward "explaining" one thing after another in cold and mechanical terms, who even feel that science squeezes the beauty and mystery out of all that it touches—to all such persons it is necessary to say: My friends, you are mistaken. Science is amazingly successful at the surface, so to speak.

But at its logical and philosophical and artistic core, it has, at least in my view, a number of limitations which can be viewed as imperfections. These are the blemishes that make science a human and endurable enterprise. These are the faults—if you will call them that—or the limitations—if you will permit a fairer term—that should allow science and art and philosophy and theology to become mutually respecting and mutually reinforcing partners.

For example, the fact that science is superbly successful at dealing with phenomena, but that it possesses the inherent defect (which I assume it shares with many other fields of thought) that it cannot furnish ultimate explanation, is, in my own view, really not a defect at all, but rather an example of the honesty and clarity that comes with maturity. And again, this defect has the virtue that it *joins* science to the rest of life, rather than separating it off in cold perfection.

Second, it is an obvious imperfection that scientists themselves do not, and apparently cannot, agree about certain of the deepest and most central aspects of science. I indicated earlier that many scientists are quite unwilling to accept the abstract type of "black-box" theory discussed here. Einstein always disliked the formal procedures of quantum theory, and persisted in thinking (if I interpret correctly) that underneath the apparently indeterministic vagary of individual atomic events was some substratum of deterministic reality (whatever that means) which science will eventually be able to reveal and understand (whatever *that* means).

But the intelligibility of the terms of the disagreement is irrelevant. For the point is that scientists—even the greatest ones in the most advanced field of physics, such as Einstein and Bohr and Planck and Dirac—cannot agree as to whether and how science explains anything.

This imperfection of science I find a most attractive one; for it reflects the fact that science is not monstrous and monolithic, but is a very human enterprise, exhibiting the same lively and useful diversity which one finds in philosophy, art, music, etc.

Thirdly, you are all aware of the nineteenth-century fear that science was in the process of imposing purely mechanistic and deterministic interpretations upon all phenomena, including ultimately the individual decisions of an individual person. And you are all aware—for this has been widely publicized—that science has itself now abandoned this view. Science recognizes that the individual events, down at the level of electrons, protons, photons, mesons, etc., are all probabilistic in character, and individually simply not predictable. Since all large-scale events—the falling of a stone, say—are ultimately composed of individual events, the large-scale events are themselves, strictly speaking, probabilistic also. But the large-scale phenomena are nevertheless dependable. The stone *does,* after all, fall. And this is simply because this large-scale event is the net result of so incredibly vast a number of small-scale events that the eccentricities always average out. Large-scale nature is, so to speak, a life insurance company with so many billion, billion, billion, billion . . . clients that she knows very precisely what fraction will die each week, even though she is completely unable to say whether or not one given individual will die.

So it is an imperfection of science, if you choose so to name it, that it is essentially statistical in nature. This means, for example, that perfect accuracy is unattainable in any measurement, that certainty is impossible in any prediction.

But does this make one admire science the less? Can you conceive of wanting to marry a woman who is completely perfect and totally predictable? Does this element of ultimate unpredictability, moreover, not remove an otherwise insuperable barrier between science and the rest of life?

My fourth defect is related to the fact that there are those who say, "I will admit that science is no doubt more strictly *logical* than any other field of intellectual activity, but logic is a cold and relentless master, and I am not so sure that I want my life dominated by it."

Logic is indeed an integral and central part of science. But logic, although a vastly useful mental tool, does not now have the reputation which it was once supposed to deserve. I have had previous occasion to write about this point, so

I will repeat here very briefly the essential conclusion of what is necessarily a somewhat technical argument.

There are two main types of logic: deductive and inductive. In the former, one starts by making a certain number of pure assumptions—technically speaking, he adopts the postulates of the system under examination. Then with the addition of a certain accepted vocabulary of signs, certain assumed formation rules for combining the signs, and certain assumed transformation rules for deriving new formulas from old ones—with this assumed machinery one then proceeds to—to do what?

Of course, all he can possibly do is to unroll, in all its lovely and unsuspected complexity, the truths—or more properly, the formally correct relationships—which were inherent in what he originally assumed. This procedure is, of course, quite powerless to create truths—it can only reveal what has been previously and unconsciously assumed.

But apart from this inherent limitation on deductive logic, which has of course been long recognized, there have rather recently been discovered, by Gödel, wholly unsuspected and startling imperfections in any system of deductive logic. Gödel has obtained two main results, each of which is of the most massive importance. He proved that it is impossible —theoretically impossible, not just unreasonably difficult— to prove the consistency of any set of postulates which is, so to speak, rich enough in content to be interesting. The question, "Is there an inner flaw in this system?" is a question which is simply unanswerable.

He also proved that any such deductive logical system inevitably has a further great limitation. Such a system is essentially incomplete. Within the system it is always possible to ask questions which are undecidable.

If deductive logic has these vital and built-in limitations, how about inductive logic, the branch of reasoning which examines all the observed cases recorded in the evidence, and seeks to induce therefrom general laws, this being the way in which the mind of man attempts to reach universals by the study of particulars. To quote from my previous paper on this subject:

Over 200 years ago David Hume bluntly denied the propriety of inductive logic. Ever since, certain skeptics have urged the necessity of practicing induction without pretending that it has any rational foundation; certain deductionists have vainly tried to prove Hume wrong; certain philosophers have optimistically hoped that a mild and friendly attitude towards such words as "rational" and "reasonable" could of itself sanction their application to statements referring to future and hence unexamined cases; and certain scientists have felt that it is vaguely sensible to suppose that future phenomena would conform to past regularities.

Deep and troublesome questions are involved here. Consider, just for a moment, the question: When and why does a single piece of past evidence give useful information about a future situation? If one takes a single piece of copper and determines that it conducts electricity, then it seems sensible to suppose that other future pieces of copper will also conduct electricity. But if we pick out a man at random and determine that his name is John, this does not at all lend credence to the idea that all other men are named John. The first of these seems to lead to a "lawlike statement," and the second to an "unlawlike" one; but no one, so far as I know, has ever been able to give workable form to this distinction.

In fact, in spite of many attempts to make induction intellectually tolerable, the matter remains a mess.

For recent researches, primarily by Dr. N. Goodman, have shown that, when strictly examined

. . . the ability of induction to deal with a future case collapses; and since this is the only useful aspect of induction, we are faced by total collapse.

Thus I must report to you that discouraging news has leaked out of the citadel of logic. The external walls appear as formidable as ever; but at the very center of the supposedly solid fortress of logical thinking, all is confusion. As practical tools, no one doubts the continuing value of the armaments. But in terms of ultimate and inner strength, the revelations are astounding indeed. The ultimate basis of both types of logical thinking is infected, at the very core, with imperfection.

Thus, one ends up by recalling Dr. Charles F. Kettering's characteristic warning "Beware of logic. It is an organized way of going wrong with confidence."

As the fifth imperfection in science I come to a topic which, because of its depth and subtlety, deserves a far more extensive and far more competent summary than I can give. This particular element of imperfection has to do with the supposed *objectivity* of science.

It is widely recognized that any natural event has a number of possible explanations. It has been demonstrated that if a certain body of experience can be usefully interpreted through one particular theory, then there is always, in fact, an infinite number of other theories each of which will equally well accommodate the same body of experience. There may be very important aesthetic reasons for preferring certain of the theories. Often, there is a tendency to accept, of the alternative explanations, the one which seems in some general sense to be "the most credible," and the "ultimate in criteria of credibility" says a recent writer,[1] "is scientific objectivity."

Careful thinkers have for long been skeptical about the supposed objectivity of so-called scientific facts. In the translator's preface to one of the master works of Poincaré, George Bruce Halsted said a half-century ago,

What is called "a knowledge of the facts" is usually merely a subjective realization that the old hypotheses are still sufficiently elastic to serve in some domain; that is, with a sufficiency of conscious or unconscious omissions and doctorings and fudgings more or less wilful.

The idea that the so-called objective facts of science may not be so sacrosanct is thus not an exclusively recent suspicion. But this idea has within the last couple of years been given an analysis that is outstanding for the clarity and honesty of its thought, for the many years of meticulous and scholarly care that were involved in the writing, and

1. Dr. Charles E. Goshen, *Saturday Review*, February 1960.

for the high and deserved reputation of its author. I refer
to Michael Polanyi's book *Personal Knowledge*.

This is a long and hard, but very rewarding book. I cannot possibly do more than make a few bold statements about
Polanyi's position, hoping that some of you will find the ideas
either interesting enough, or shocking enough, or both, so
that you will read the book.

He totally rejects the ideal of scientific detachment. He
does not believe that knowledge is, or can be, impersonal,
universally established, completely detached, objective. He
regards knowing as an act of comprehension that involves
change in the person carrying out the act of comprehension.
Thus comprehension is essentially an irreversible process,
and is noncritical in the sense that there is no permanently
fixed framework within which critical testing can occur.
On the other hand, he does not consider knowledge to be
wholly subjective. He does believe that active and skillful
comprehension can establish contact with "a hidden reality,"
and it is this strange and almost mystic blend of passionate
contribution in the personal act of knowing, together with a
thereby established contact with objective reality, which he
designates as *personal knowledge*. "Even in the exact sciences
'knowing' is an art, of which the skill of the knower, guided
by his passionate sense of increasing contact with reality,
is a logically necessary part."

We have spoken thus far of five imperfect aspects of
science. Let us summarize the view necessitated by these
five points.

Science has, as a tool for dealing with nature, proved to
be superbly successful. With respect to physical nature, and
at all moderate scales of space or time—say larger than an
atom and smaller than a galaxy, say more persistent than
10^{-10} seconds and less than a billion years—science seems
to have unlimited ability. With the extremely small or the
extremely large, with inconceivably brief or extended phenomena, science has a difficult time. It is by no means clear
that our present concepts or even our existing language is
suitable for these ranges. In the realm of animate matter,
science has made wonderful, but more limited, progress.

And we can, at the present, see no fixed barriers to further progress.

We must agree that all this adds up to a very great intellectual achievement—very possibly the greatest that man has, as yet, to his credit.

But if one looks deeply within this system, instead of encountering a harder and harder inner core, instead of meeting more and more dependable precision, more and more rigidity, compulsion, and finality, instead of finally reaching permanence and perfection, what does one find?

He finds unresolved and apparently unresolvable disagreement among scientists concerning the relationship of scientific thought to reality—and concerning the nature and meaning of reality itself. He finds that the explanations of science have utility, but that they do in sober fact not explain. He finds the old external appearance of inevitability completely vanished, for he discovers a charming capriciousness in all the individual events. He finds that logic, so generally supposed to be infallible and unassailable, is in fact shaky and incomplete. He finds that the whole concept of objective truth is a will-o-the-wisp.

For those who have been deluded, by external appearances and by partial understanding, into thinking of science as a relentless, all-conquering intellectual force, armed with finality and perfection, the limitations treated here would have to be considered as damaging imperfections. You will have realized, however, from the pride and enthusiasm with which I have exhibited these points, that I do not myself think of them as unpleasant imperfections, but rather as the blemishes which make our mistress all the more endearing.

And this remark leads at once to the final point—the fault which I do in fact consider a serious imperfection. This is not a weakness which is inherent in the nature of science, but one which has been created by the attitude of scientists and non-scientists alike.

I refer to the fact that many scientists—and the public which they have over and falsely impressed—have created a horrid and dangerous gap between science and the rest of life. This is the tragedy of the "Two Cultures," which have been so brilliantly discussed by C. P. Snow. "I believe," says this scientist who is also a distinguished essayist and novelist, "the intellectual life of the whole of western society is increasingly being split into two polar groups."

The two cultures referred to by Snow are formed, on the one hand, of the scientist and the very few non-scientists who have bothered to understand science and its role in modern life, and on the other hand, of the literary intellectuals, the artists—in a broad sense the humanists. Snow comments that "thirty years ago the cultures had long ceased to speak to each other: but at least they managed a kind of frozen smile across the gulf. Now the politeness is gone, and they just make faces."

Snow seems to place a rather greater blame for this perilous dichotomy upon the literary intellectuals, whom he considers the more seriously impoverished because of the scorn which motivates their attitude towards science.

I am myself more inclined to place the greater blame upon the scientists. Although some scientists seem almost childishly eager to leave their laboratories to talk about things which they do *not* understand, they have been pretty reluctant to leave their laboratories to talk and write intelligently about what they *do* superbly understand.

But there is blame enough for all elements of society to deserve a substantial portion; and allocation of the blame is not a constructive task. What we must do—scientists and non-scientists alike—is close the gap. We must bring science back into life as a human enterprise, an enterprise that has at its core the uncertainty, the flexibility, the subjectivity, the sweet unreasonableness, the dependence upon creativity and faith which permit it, when properly understood, to take its place as a friendly and understanding companion to all the rest of life.

Huxley and Weaver offer a picture of what science
is and what it cannot claim to be. On a purely practical
level, true science has proved to be the greatest success
of the modern world, and like all successes it has attracted bogus practitioners. In the damage they do, they are
akin to the antiscientists, who find no validity in the scientific process. Although the highly educated may find their
contentions laughable, there is a huge undercurrent of ignorance and superstition on which they feed. Gardner is a regular
contributor to the Scientific American. He shows that this ever-
present undercurrent remains as potentially dangerous, in these
presumably enlightened times, as in the darkest ages of the
past.

IN THE NAME OF SCIENCE

MARTIN GARDNER

ONE CURIOUS CONSEQUENCE of the current boom in science is the rise of the promoter of new and strange "scientific" theories. He is riding into prominence, so to speak, on
the coat-tails of reputable investigators. The scientists themselves, of course, pay very little attention to him. They are
too busy with more important matters. But the less informed
general public, hungry for sensational discoveries and quick
panaceas, often provides him with a noisy and enthusiastic
following.

In 1951, tens of thousands of mentally ill people throughout the country entered "dianetic reveries" in which they
moved back along their "time track" and tried to recall unpleasant experiences they had when they were embryos.
Thousands of more sophisticated neurotics, who regard
dianetics as the invention of a mountebank, are now sitting
in "orgone boxes" to raise their body's charge of "orgone
energy." Untold numbers of middle-aged housewives are

preparing to live to the age of 100 by a diet rich in yoghurt, wheat-germ, and blackstrap-molasses.

Not only in the fields of mental and physical health is the spurious scientist flourishing. A primitive interpretation of Old Testament miracle tales, which one thought went out of fashion with the passing of William Jennings Bryan, has received a powerful shot in the arm. Has not the eminent "astrophysicist," Dr. Immanuel Velikovsky, established the fact that the earth stopped rotating precisely at the moment Joshua commanded the sun and moon to stand still? For fifty years, geologists and physicists have been combining forces to perfect complex, delicate instruments for exploring underground structures. They've been wasting their time according to Kenneth Roberts, the well-known novelist. All you need is a forked twig, and he has written a persuasive and belligerent book to prove it.

Since flying saucers were first reported, countless individuals have been convinced that the earth is under observation by visitors from another planet, that the mysterious disks are piloted by inhabitants of Venus who are exact duplicates of earthlings except they are three feet tall. A study by Gerald Heard makes out an even stronger case for believing the saucers are controlled by intelligent bees from Mars.

It is all very amusing, one might say, to titillate public fancy with books about bee people from Mars. The scientists are not fooled, nor are readers who are scientifically informed. If the public wants to shell out cash for such flummery, what difference does it make? The answer is that it is not at all amusing when people are misled by scientific claptrap. Thousands of neurotics desperately in need of trained psychiatric care are seriously retarding their therapy by dalliance with crank cults. Already a frightening number of cases have come to light of suicides and mental crack-ups among patients undergoing these dubious cures. No reputable publisher would think of releasing a book describing a treatment for cancer if it were written by a doctor universally considered a quack by his peers. Yet the difference between such a book and *Dianetics* is not very great.

What about the long-run effects of non-medical books like Velikovsky's, and the treatises on flying saucers? It is hard to see how the effects can be anything but harmful. Who can say how many orthodox Christians and Jews read *Worlds in Collision* and drifted back into a cruder Biblicism because they were told that science had reaffirmed the Old Testament miracles? Mencken once wrote that if you heave an egg out of a Pullman car window anywhere in the United States you are likely to hit a fundamentalist. That was years ago, and times have changed, but it is easy to forget how far from won is the battle against religious superstition. It is easy to forget that thousands of high school teachers of biology, in many of our southern states, are still afraid to teach the theory of evolution for fear of losing their jobs.

An even more regrettable effect produced by the publication of scientific rubbish is the confusion they sow in the minds of gullible readers about what is and what isn't scientific knowledge. And the more the public is confused, the easier it falls prey to doctrines of pseudo-science which may at some future date receive the backing of politically powerful groups. A renaissance of German quasi-science paralleled the rise of Hitler. If the German people had been better trained to distinguish good from bad science, would they have swallowed so easily the insane racial theories of the Nazi anthropologists?

In the last analysis, the best means of combating the spread of pseudo-science is an enlightened public, able to distinguish the work of a reputable investigator from the work of the incompetent and self-deluded. This is not as hard to do as one might think. Of course, there always will be borderline cases hard to classify, but the fact that black shades into white through many shades of gray does not mean that the distinction between black and white is difficult.

Actually, two different "continuums" are involved. One is a scale of the degree to which a scientific theory is confirmed by evidence. At one end of this scale are theories almost certainly false, such as the dianetic view that a one-day-old embryo can make sound recordings of its mother's conversation. Toward the middle of the scale are theories advanced as working hypotheses, but highly debatable because of the lack of sufficient data. Finally, at the other extreme of the scale, are theories almost certainly true, such as the belief that the earth is round or that men and beasts are distant cousins. The problem of determining the degree to which a theory is confirmed is extremely difficult and technical, and, as a matter of fact, there are no known methods for giving precise "probability values" to hypotheses. This problem, however, need not trouble us. We shall be concerned only with theories so close to "almost certainly false" that there is no reasonable doubt about their worthlessness.

The second continuum is the scale of scientific competence. It also has its extremes—ranging from obviously admirable scientists, to men of equally obvious incompetence. That there are individuals of debatable status—men whose theories are on the borderline of sanity, men competent in one field and not in others, men competent at one period of life and not at others, and so on—all this ought not to blind us to the obvious fact that there is a type of self-styled scientist who can legitimately be called a crank. It is not the novelty of his views or the neurotic motivations behind his work that provide the grounds for calling him this. The grounds are the technical criteria by which theories are evaluated. If a man persists in advancing views that are contradicted by all available evidence, and which offer no reasonable grounds for serious consideration, he will rightfully be dubbed a crank by his colleagues.

Cranks vary widely in both knowledge and intelligence. Some are stupid, ignorant, almost illiterate men who confine their activities to sending "crank letters" to prominent scientists. Some produce crudely written pamphlets, usually published by the author himself, with long titles, and pictures of the author on the cover. Still others are brilliant and well-educated, often with an excellent understanding of the branch of science in which they are speculating. Their books can be highly deceptive imitations of the genuine article—well-written and impressively learned. In spite of these wide variations, however, most pseudo-scientists have a number of characteristics in common.

First and most important of these traits is that cranks work in almost total isolation from their colleagues. Not isolation in the geographical sense, but in the sense of having no fruitful contacts with fellow researchers. In the Renaissance, this isolation was not necessarily a sign of the crank. Science was poorly organized. There were no journals or societies. Communication among workers in a field was often very difficult. Moreover, there frequently were enormous social pressures operating against such communication. In the classic case of Galileo, the Inquisition forced him into isolation because the Church felt his views were undermining religious faith. Even as late as Darwin's time, the pressure of religious conservatism was so great that Darwin and a handful of admirers stood almost alone against the opinions of more respectable biologists.

Today, these social conditions no longer obtain. The battle of science to free itself from religious control has been almost completely won. Church groups still oppose certain doctrines in biology and psychology, but even this opposition no longer dominates scientific bodies or journals. Efficient networks of communication within each science have been established. A vast cooperative process of testing new theories is constantly going on—a process amazingly free (except, of course, in totalitarian nations) from control by a higher "orthodoxy." In this modern framework, in which scientific progress has become dependent on the constant give and take of data, it is impossible for a working scientist to be isolated.

The modern crank insists that his isolation is not desired on his part. It is due, he claims, to the prejudice of established scientific groups against new ideas. Nothing could be further from the truth. Scientific journals today are filled with bizarre theories. Often the quickest road to fame is to overturn a firmly-held belief. Einstein's work on relativity is the outstanding example. Although it met with considerable opposition at first, it was on the whole an intelligent opposition. With few exceptions, none of Einstein's reputable opponents dismissed him as a crackpot. They could not so dismiss him because for years he contributed brilliant articles to the journals and had won wide recognition as a theoretical physicist. In a surprisingly short time, his relativity theories won almost universal acceptance, and one of the greatest revolutions in the history of science quietly took place.

It would be foolish, of course, to deny that history contains many sad examples of novel scientific views which did not receive an unbiased hearing, and which later proved to be true. The pseudo-scientist never tires reminding his readers of these cases. The opposition of traditional psychology to the study of hypnotic phenomena (accentuated by the fact that Mesmer was both a crank and a charlatan) is an outstanding instance. In the field of medicine, the germ theory of Pasteur, the use of anesthetics, and Dr. Semmelweiss' insistence that doctors sterilize their hands before attending childbirth are other well-known examples of theories which met with strong professional prejudice.

Probably the most notorious instance of scientific stubbornness was the refusal of eighteenth-century astronomers to believe that stones actually fell from the sky. Reaction against medieval superstitions and old wives' tales was still so strong that whenever a meteor fell, astronomers insisted it had either been picked up somewhere and carried by the wind, or that the persons who claimed to see it fall were lying. Even the great French *Académie des Sciences* ridiculed this folk belief, in spite of a number of early studies of meteoric phenomena. Not until April 26, 1803, when several thousand small meteors fell on the town of L'Aigle, France, did the astronomers decide to take falling rocks seriously.

Many other examples of scientific traditionalism might be cited, as well as cases of important contributions made by persons of a crank variety. The discovery of the law of conservation of energy by Robert Mayer, a psychotic German physician, is a classic instance. Occasionally a layman, completely outside of science, will make an astonishingly prophetic guess—like Swift's prediction about the moons of Mars, or Samuel Johnson's belief (expressed in a letter, in 1781, more than eighty years before the discovery of germs) that microbes were the cause of dysentery.

One must be extremely cautious, however, before comparing the work of some contemporary eccentric with any of these earlier examples, so frequently cited in crank writings. In medicine, we must remember, it is only in the last fifty years or so that the art of healing has become anything resembling a rigorous scientific discipline. One can go back to periods in which medicine was in its infancy, hopelessly mixed with superstition, and find endless cases of scientists with unpopular views that later proved correct. The same holds true of other sciences. But the picture today is vastly different. The prevailing spirit among scientists, outside of totalitarian countries, is one of eagerness for fresh ideas. In the great search for a cancer cure now going on, not the slightest stone, however curious its shape, is being left unturned. If anything, scientific journals err on the side of permitting *questionable* theses to be published, so they may be discussed and checked in the hope of finding something of value. A few years ago a student at the Institute for Advanced Studies in Princeton was asked how his seminar had been that day. He was quoted in a news magazine as exclaiming, "Wonderful! Everything we knew about physics last week isn't true!"

Here and there, of course—especially among older scientists who, like everyone else, have a natural tendency to become set in their opinions—one may occasionally meet with irrational prejudice against a new point of view. You cannot blame a scientist for unconsciously resisting a theory which may, in some cases, render his entire life's work obsolete. Even the great Galileo refused to accept Kepler's theory, long after the evidence was quite strong, that planets move in ellipses. Fortunately there are always, in the words of Alfred Noyes, "The young, swift-footed, waiting for the fire," who can form the vanguard of scientific revolutions.

It must also be admitted that in certain areas of science, where empirical data are still hazy, a point of view may acquire a kind of cult following and harden into rigid dogma. Modifications of Einstein's theory, for example, sometimes meet a resistance similar to that which met the original theory. And no doubt the reader will have at least one acquaintance for whom a particular brand of psychoanalysis has become virtually a religion, and who waxes highly indignant if its postulates are questioned by adherents of a rival brand.

Actually, a certain degree of dogma—of pig-headed orthodoxy—is both necessary and desirable for the health of science. It forces the scientist with a novel view to mass considerable evidence before his theory can be seriously entertained. If this situation did not exist, science would be reduced to shambles by having to examine every newfangled notion that came along. Clearly, working scientists have more important tasks. If someone announces that the moon is made of green cheese, the professional astronomer cannot be expected to climb down from his telescope and write a detailed refutation.

The modern pseudo-scientist—to return to the point from which we have digressed—stands entirely outside the closely integrated channels through which new ideas are introduced and evaluated. He works in isolation. He does not send his findings to the recognized journals, or if he does, they are rejected for reasons which in the vast majority of cases are excellent. In most cases the crank is not well enough informed to write a paper with even a surface resemblance to a significant study. As a consequence, he finds himself excluded from the journals and societies, and almost universally ignored by the competent workers in his field. In fact, the reputable scientist does not even know of the crank's existence unless his work is given widespread publicity through non-academic channels, or unless the scientist makes a hobby of collecting crank literature. The eccentric is forced, therefore, to tread a lonely way. He speaks before organizations he himself has founded, contributes to journals he himself may edit, and—until recently—publishes books only when he or his followers can raise sufficient funds to have them printed privately.

A second characteristic of the pseudo-scientist, which greatly strengthens his isolation, is a tendency toward paranoia. It is easy to understand that a strong sense of personal greatness must be involved whenever a crank stands in solitary, bitter opposition to every recognized authority in his field.

If the self-styled scientist is rationalizing strong religious convictions, as often is the case, his paranoid drives may be reduced to a minimum. The desire to bolster religious beliefs with science can be a powerful motive. For example, in examination of George McCready Price, the greatest of modern opponents of evolution, his devout faith in Seventh Day Adventism is a sufficient explanation for his curious geological views. But even in such cases, an element of paranoia is nearly always present. Otherwise the pseudo-scientist would lack the stamina to fight a vigorous, single-handed battle against such overwhelming odds.

There are five ways in which the sincere pseudo-scientist's paranoid tendencies are likely to be exhibited.

1] He considers himself a genius.

2] He regards his colleagues, without exception, as ignorant blockheads. Everyone is out of step except himself. Frequently he insults his opponents by accusing them of stupidity, dishonesty, or other base motives. If they ignore him, he takes this to mean his arguments are unanswerable. If they retaliate in kind, this strengthens his delusion that he is battling scoundrels.

3] He believes himself unjustly persecuted and discriminated against. The recognized societies refuse to let him lecture. The journals reject his papers and either ignore his books or assign them to "enemies" for review. It is all part of a dastardly plot. It never occurs to the crank that this opposition may be due to error in his work. It springs solely, he is convinced, from blind prejudice on the part of the established hierarchy—the high priests of science who fear to have their orthodoxy overthrown.

Vicious slanders and unprovoked attacks, he usually insists, are constantly being made against him. He likens himself to Bruno, Galileo, Copernicus, Pasteur, and other great men who were unjustly persecuted for their heresies. If he has had no formal training in the field in which he works, he will attribute this persecution to a scientific masonry, unwilling to admit into its inner sanctums anyone who has not gone through the proper initiation rituals. He repeatedly calls your attention to important scientific discoveries made by laymen.

4]   He has strong compulsions to focus his attacks on the greatest scientists and the best-established theories. When Newton was the outstanding name in physics, eccentric works in that science were violently anti-Newton. Today, with Einstein the father-symbol of authority, a crank theory of physics is likely to attack Einstein in the name of Newton. This same defiance can be seen in a tendency to assert the diametrical opposite of well-established beliefs. Mathematicians prove the angle cannot be trisected. So the crank trisects it. A perpetual motion machine cannot be built. He builds one. There are many eccentric theories in which the "pull" of gravity is replaced by a "push." Germs do not cause disease, some modern cranks insist. Disease produces the germs. Glasses do not help the eyes, said Dr. Bates. They make them worse. Cyrus Teed literally turned the entire cosmos inside-out, compressing it within the confines of a hollow earth, inhabited only on the inside.

5]   He often has a tendency to write in a complex jargon, in many cases making use of terms and phrases he himself has coined. Schizophrenics sometimes talk in what psychiatrists call "neologisms"—words which have meaning to the patient, but sound like Jabberwocky to everyone else. Many of the classics of crackpot science exhibit a neologistic tendency.

When the crank's I.Q. is low, as in the case of the late Wilbur Glenn Voliva who thought the earth shaped like a pancake, he rarely achieves much of a following. But if he is a brilliant thinker, he is capable of developing incredibly complex theories. He will be able to defend them in books of vast erudition, with profound observations, and often

liberal portions of sound science. His rhetoric may be enormously persuasive. All the parts of his world usually fit
together beautifully, like a jig-saw puzzle. It is impossible
to get the best of him in any type of argument. He has
anticipated all your objections. He counters them with unexpected answers of great ingenuity. Even on the subject of
the shape of the earth, a layman may find himself powerless in a debate with a flat-earther. George Bernard Shaw,
in *Everybody's Political What's What?*, gives an hilarious
description of a meeting at which a flat-earth speaker completely silenced all opponents who raised objections from
the floor. "Opposition such as no atheist could have provoked assailed him"; writes Shaw, "and he, having heard
their arguments hundreds of times, played skittles with them,
lashing the meeting into a spluttering fury as he answered
easily what it considered unanswerable."

The amount of intellectual energy that has been wasted
on these lost causes is almost unbelievable. It is amusing—
at times frightening—to witness the grotesque extremes to
which deluded scientists can be misled, and the extremes to
which they in turn can mislead others. Their disciples are
often intelligent and sometimes eminent men—men not well
enough informed on the subject in question to penetrate the
Master's counterfeit trappings, and who frequently find in
their devotion an outlet for their own neurotic rebellions.

Just as an experienced doctor is able to diagnose certain
ailments the instant a new patient walks into his office, or
a police officer learns to recognize criminal types from
subtle behavior clues which escape the untrained eye, so
we, perhaps, may learn to recognize the future scientific
crank when we first encounter him.

And encounter him we shall. If the present trend continues, we can expect a wide variety of these men, with
theories yet unimaginable, to put in their appearance in the
years immediately ahead. They will write impressive books,
give inspiring lectures, organize exciting cults. They may
achieve a following of one—or one million. In any case,
it will be well for ourselves and for society if we are on our
guard against them.

B. Observation, Hypothesis, Experiment

*Only if we understand the scientist himself, examine his mo-
tivations and see him actually observing, forming hypotheses,
testing them by controlled experiment, and having those flashes
of inspiration which are genius or akin to it, can we truly
understand science.*

*The faculty of observation, as opposed to the process of
merely "looking at," is one of the scientist's basic weapons.
It plays a fundamental role in all scientific activity. The great
contribution of Francis Bacon to the advancement of knowledge was his insistence on the importance of observed fact. He
has been rightly criticized for failure to give due credit to the
other elements in scientific creation—the faculty of wonder,
for example—but his emphasis on what actually does exist in
nature, as opposed to what ought to exist—the rationalization
of the Greeks—must be accepted if science is to have any
validity.*

*In "How Agassiz Taught Me to See," we are introduced to
two great observers who were also outstanding personalities in
American science. Louis Agassiz was born in Switzerland in
1807 and won a reputation as a natural scientist before immi-
grating to the United States. He became professor of zoology
and geology at Harvard in 1848, and although he was one of
the foremost opponents of Darwinian theory, his reputation,
his charm, and his ability to inspire his students greatly stimulated the fledgling science of his adopted country. Agassiz, who
was a geologist, a paleontologist, and an ichthyologist, was an
observer of the best type. His method of teaching his techniques to his students is graphically portrayed in this selection
by Nathaniel Shaler. Shaler was born in Kentucky in 1841.
Before studying with Agassiz he fought in the Civil War, but
became so weakened by the hazards of army service that he
was invalided out. Later his interests centered on paleontology
and geology. He made adventurous field trips to some of the
most uncivilized parts of the earth, and wrote scores of books*

and articles. He became a full professor at twenty-eight, and
his flamboyant personality, combined with the human interest
of his lectures, made him the most popular teacher at Harvard.
His influence on his students was, like that of Agassiz, one of
his main contributions to American science.

HOW AGASSIZ TAUGHT ME TO SEE

NATHANIEL SHALER

WHEN I FIRST MET Louis Agassiz, he was still in the
prime of his admirable manhood; though he was then fifty-
two years old, and had passed his constructive period, he still
had the look of a young man. His face was the most genial
and engaging that I had ever seen and his manner capti-
vated me altogether. But as I had been among men who had
a free swing, and for a year among people who seemed to
me to be cold and super-rational, hungry as I doubtless
was for human sympathy, Agassiz's welcome went to my
heart—I was at once his captive. It has been my good
chance to see many men of engaging presence and ways,
but I have never known his equal.

As my account of Agassiz's quality should rest upon my
experiences with him, I shall now go on to tell how and
to what effect he trained me. In that day there were no
written examinations on any subjects to which candidates
for the Lawrence Scientific School had to pass. The professors in charge of the several departments questioned the
candidates and determined their fitness to pursue the course
of study they desired to undertake. Few or none who had
any semblance of an education were denied admission to
Agassiz's laboratory. At that time, the instructors had, in
addition to their meager salaries—his was then $2500 per
annum—the regular fees paid in by the students under his
charge. So I was promptly assured that I was admitted. Be

it said, however, that he did give me an effective oral examination, which, as he told me, was intended to show whether I could expect to go forward to a degree at the end of four years of study. On this matter of the degree he was obdurate, refusing to recommend some who had been with him for many years and had succeeded in their special work, giving as reason for his denial that they were "too ignorant."

While Agassiz questioned me carefully as to what I had read and what I had seen, he seemed in this preliminary going over in no wise concerned to find what I knew about fossils, rocks, animals, and plants; he put aside the offerings of my scanty lore. This offended me a bit, as I recall, for the reason that I thought I knew, and for a self-taught lad really did know, a good deal about such matters, especially as to the habits of insects, particularly spiders. It seemed hard to be denied the chance to make my parade; but I afterward saw what this meant, that he did not intend to let me begin my tasks by posing as a naturalist. The beginning was indeed quite different, and, as will be seen, in a manner that quickly evaporated my conceit. It was made and continued in a way I will now recount.

Agassiz's laboratory was then in a rather small two-storied building, looking much like a square dwelling-house, which stood where the College Gymnasium now stands. In this primitive establishment Agassiz's laboratory, as distinguished from the storerooms where the collections were crammed, occupied one room about thirty feet long and fifteen feet wide—what is now the west room on the lower floor of the edifice. In this place, already packed, I had assigned to me a small pine table with a rusty tin pan upon it.

When I sat me down before my tin pan, Agassiz brought me a small fish, placing it before me with the rather stern requirement that I should study it, but should on no account talk to anyone concerning it, nor read anything relating to fishes, until I had his permission so to do. To my inquiry "What shall I do?" he said in effect: "Find out what you can without damaging the specimen; when I think that

you have done the work I will question you." In the course
of an hour I thought I had compassed that fish; it was
rather an unsavory object, giving forth the stench of old
alcohol, then loathsome to me, though in time I came to like
it. Many of the scales were loosened so that they fell off. It
appeared to me to be a case for a summary report, which
I was anxious to make and get on to the next stage of the
business. But Agassiz, though always within call, concerned
himself no further with me that day, nor the next, nor
for a week. At first, this neglect was distressing; but I saw
that it was a game, for he was, as I discerned rather than
saw, covertly watching me. So I set my wits to work upon
the thing, and in the course of a hundred hours or so thought
I had done much—a hundred times as much as seemed
possible at the start. I got interested in finding out how the
scales went in series, their shape, the form and placement of
the teeth, etc. Finally, I felt full of the subject and probably expressed it in my bearing; as for words about it then,
there were none from my master except his cheery "good
morning." At length on the seventh day, came the question
"Well?" and my disgorge of learning to him as he sat on the
edge of my table puffing his cigar. At the end of the hour's
telling, he swung off and away, saying. "That is not right."
Here I began to think that after all perhaps the rules for
scanning Latin verse were not the worst infliction in the
world. Moreover, it was clear that he was playing a game
with me to find if I were capable of doing hard, continuous
work without the support of a teacher, and this stimulated
me to labor. I went at the task anew, discarded my first
notes, and in another week of ten hours a day labor I had
results which astonished myself and satisfied him. Still there
was no trace of praise in words or manner. He signified that
it would do by placing before me about a half a peck of
bones, telling me to see what I could make of them, with
no further directions to guide me. I soon found that they
were the skeletons of half a dozen fishes of different species;
the jaws told me that much at a first inspection. The task
evidently was to fit the separate bones together in their
proper order. Two months or more went to this task with no

other help than an occasional looking over my grouping with the stereotyped remark: "That is not right." Finally, the task was done and I was again set upon alcoholic specimens —this time a remarkable lot of specimens representing, perhaps, twenty species of the side-swimmers or *Pleuronectidæ*.

I shall never forget the sense of power in dealing with things which I felt in beginning the more extended work on a group of animals. I had learned the art of comparing objects, which is the basis of the naturalist's work. At this stage I was allowed to read and to discuss my work with others about me. I did both eagerly, and acquired a considerable knowledge of the literature of ichthyology, becoming especially interested in the system of classification, then most imperfect. I tried to follow Agassiz's scheme of division into the order of ctenoids and ganoids, with the result that I found one of my species of side-swimmers had cycloid scales on one side and ctenoid on the other. This not only shocked my sense of the value of classification in a way that permitted of no full recovery of my original respect for the process, but for a time shook my confidence in my master's knowledge. At the same time I had a malicious pleasure in exhibiting my *find* to him, expecting to repay in part the humiliation which he had evidently tried to inflict on my conceit. To my question as to how the nondescript should be classified he said: "My boy, there are now two of us who know that."

This incident of the fish made an end of my novitiate. After that, with a suddenness of transition which puzzled me, Agassiz became very communicative; we passed indeed into the relation of friends of like age and purpose.

Henri Fabre was a naturalist of the last century who, although he received no formal instruction in the art, was characterized by Charles Darwin as "the incomparable observer." A poor boy who sprang from "plowmen, rye-sowers, cattle drovers," he

*was born in France in 1823 and became an impoverished
schoolmaster. He had an insatiable desire to know and educated himself in mathematics and the natural sciences. He was
a writer of exceptional charm; his books introduced generations
of school children to the world of life. His genius for observation was combined with a monumental patience. He would sit
for hours or days watching the antics of almost invisible insects. He relates that on one occasion, three women, vine pick-
ers, passed him at daybreak sitting on a stone and apparently
doing nothing. At sunset he was in the same position. He heard
one woman whisper, "Un paouré inoucènt, pécaïre!" and all
three crossed themselves and hurried on. Fabre failed to make
any great contribution to biological science, but he was, like
Huxley, one of the great educators of the nineteenth century.
Even today his nature studies are read with delight. "The
Courtship of the Scorpion" reveals the meticulousness with
which he observed every small detail of insect life.*

THE COURTSHIP OF THE SCORPION

J. HENRI FABRE

IN APRIL, when the Swallow returns to us and the
Cuckoo sounds his first note, a revolution takes place among
my hitherto peaceable Scorpions. Several whom I have
established in the colony in the enclosure, leave their shelter
at nightfall, go wandering about and do not return to their
homes. A more serious business: often, under the same
stone, are two Scorpions of whom one is in the act of
devouring the other. Is this a case of brigandage among
creatures of the same order, who, falling into vagabond ways
when the fine weather sets in thoughtlessly enter their
neighbors' houses and there meet with their undoing unless
they be the stronger? One would almost think it, so quickly

is the intruder eaten up, for days at a time and in small
mouthfuls, even as the usual game would be.

Now here is something to give us a hint. The Scorpions
devoured are invariably of middling size. Their lighter
coloring, their less protuberant bellies, mark them as males,
always males. The others, larger, more paunchy and a little
darker in shade, do not end in this unhappy fashion. So
these are probably not brawls between neighbors who,
jealous of their solitude, would soon settle the hash of any
visitor and eat him afterwards, a drastic method of putting
a stop to further indiscretions; they are rather nuptial rites,
tragically performed by the matron after pairing. To determine how much ground there is for this suspicion is beyond
my powers until next year: I am still too badly equipped.

Spring returns once more. I have prepared the large glass
cage in advance and stocked it with twenty-five inhabitants,
each with his bit of crockery. From mid-April onwards,
every evening, when it grows dark, between seven and
nine o'clock, great animation reigns in the crystal palace.
That which seemed deserted by day now becomes a scene
of festivity. As soon as supper is finished, the whole household runs out to look on. A lantern hung outside the panes
allows us to follow events.

These hideous devotees of gaiety provide a dance that is
not wholly devoid of charm. Some come from afar; solemnly
they emerge from the shadow; then, suddenly, with a rush
as swift and easy as a slide, they join the crowd, in the
light. Their agility reminds one of mice scurrying along
with their tiny steps. They seek one another and fly
precipitately the moment they touch, as though they had
mutually burnt their fingers. Others, after tumbling about a
little with their play-fellows, make off hurriedly, wildly.
They take fresh courage in the dark and return. At times,
there is a violent tumult: a confused mass of swarming legs,
snapping claws, tails curving and clashing, threatening or
fondling, it is hard to say which. In this affray, under
favorable conditions, twin specks of light flare and shine like
carbuncles. One would take them for eyes that emit flash-
ing glances; in reality they are two polished, reflecting

facets, which occupy the front of the head. All, large and small alike, take part in the brawl; it might be a battle to the death, a general massacre; and it is just a wanton frolic. Even so do kittens bemaul each other. Soon, the group disperses; all make off in all sorts of directions, without a scratch, without a sprain.

Behold the fugitives collecting once more beneath the lantern. They pass and pass again; they come and go, often meeting front to front. He who is in the greatest hurry walks over the back of the other, who lets him have his way without any protest but a movement of the body. It is no time for blows; at most, two Scorpions meeting will exchange a cuff, that is to say, a rap of the caudal staff. In their community, this friendly thump, in which the point of the sting plays no part, is a sort of a fisticuff in frequent use. There are better things than entangled legs and brandished tails; there are sometimes poses of the highest originality. Face to face, with claws drawn back, two wrestlers proceed to stand on their heads like acrobats, that is to say, resting only on the fore-quarters, they raise the whole hinder portion of the body, so much so that the chest displays the four little lung pockets uncovered. Then the tails, held vertically erect in a straight line, exchange mutual rubs, gliding one over the other, while their extremities are hooked together and repeatedly fastened and unfastened. Suddenly, the friendly pyramid falls to pieces and each runs off hurriedly, without ceremony.

What were these two wrestlers trying to do, in their eccentric posture? Was it a set-to between two rivals? It would seem not, so peaceful is the encounter. My subsequent observations were to tell me that this was the mutual teasing of a betrothed couple. To declare his flame, the Scorpion stands on his head.

To continue as I have begun and give a homogeneous picture of the thousand tiny particulars gathered day by day would have its advantages; the story would sooner be told; but, at the same time deprived of its details, which vary greatly between one observation and the next and are difficult to piece together, it would be less interesting.

Nothing must be neglected in the relation of manners so strange and as yet so little known. At the risk of repeating one's self here and there, it is preferable to adhere to chronological order and to tell the story by fragments, as one's observations reveal fresh facts. Order will emerge from this disorder; for each of the more remarkable evenings supplies some feature that corroborates and completes those which go before. I will therefore continue my narration in the form of a diary.

25th April, 1904.   Hullo! What is this, something I have not yet seen? My eyes, ever on the watch, look upon the affair for the first time. Two Scorpions face each other, with claws outstretched and fingers clasped. It is a question of a friendly grasp of the hand and not the prelude to a battle, for the two partners are behaving to each other in the most peaceful way. There is one of either sex. One is paunchy and browner than the other: this is the female; the other is comparatively slim and pale: this is the male. With their tails prettily curled, the couple stroll with measured steps along the pane. The male is ahead and walks backwards, without jolt or jerk, without any resistance to overcome. The female follows obediently, clasped by her finger-tips and face to face with her leader.

The stroll is interrupted by halts that do not affect the method of conjunction; it is resumed, now here, now there, from end to end of the enclosure. Nothing shows the object which the strollers have in view. They loiter, they dawdle, they most certainly exchange ogling glances. Even so in my village, on Sundays, after vespers, do the youth of both sexes saunter along the hedges, every Jack with his Jill.

Often they tack about. It is always the male who decides which fresh direction the pair shall take. Without releasing her hands, he turns gracefully to the left or right about and places himself side by side with companion. Then, for a moment, with tail laid flat, he strokes her spine. The other stands motionless, impassive.

For over an hour, without tiring, I watch these interminable comings and goings. A part of the household lends me its eyes in the presence of the strange sight which no one in the world has yet seen, at least with a vision capable of observing. In spite of the lateness of the hour, which upsets all our habits, our attention is concentrated and no essential thing escapes us.

At last, about ten o'clock, something happens. The male has hit upon a potsherd whose shelter seems to suit him. He releases his companion with one hand, with one alone, and continuing to hold her with the other, he scratches with his legs and sweeps with his tail. A grotto opens. He enters and, slowly, without violence, drags the patient Scorpioness after him. Soon both have disappeared. A plug of sand closes the dwelling. The couple are at home.

To disturb them would be a blunder: I should be interfering too soon, at an inopportune moment, if I tried at once to see what was happening below. The preliminary stages may last for the best part of the night; and it does not do for me, who have turned eighty, to sit up so late. I feel my legs giving way; and my eyes seem full of sand.

All night long I dream of Scorpions. They crawl under my bedclothes, they pass over my face; and I am not particularly excited, so many curious things do I see in my imagination. The next morning, at daybreak, I lift the stoneware. The female is alone. Of the male there is no trace, either in the home or in the neighborhood. First disappointment, to be followed by many others.

10th May. It is nearly seven o'clock in the evening; the sky is overcast with signs of an approaching shower. Under one of the potsherds is a motionless couple, face to face, with linked fingers. Cautiously I raise the potsherd and leave the occupants uncovered, so as to study the consequences of the interview at my ease. The darkness of the night falls and nothing, it seems to me, will disturb the calm of the home deprived of its roof. A sharp shower compels me to retire. They, under the lid of the cage, have no need to take shelter against the rain. What will they do, left to their business as they are but deprived of a canopy to their alcove?

An hour later, the rain ceases and I return to my Scorpions. They are gone. They have taken up their abode under a neighboring tile. Still with their fingers linked, the female is outside and the male indoors, preparing the home. At intervals of ten minutes, the members of my family relieve one another so as not to lose the exact moment of the pairing, which appears to be imminent. Wasted pains: at eight o'clock, it being now quite dark, the couple, dissatisfied with the spot, set out on a fresh ramble, hand in hand, and go prospecting elsewhere. The male, walking backwards, leads the way, chooses the dwelling as he pleases; the female follows with docility. It is an exact repetition of what I saw on the 25th of April.

At last a tile is found to suit them. The male goes in first but this time neither hand releases his companion for a moment. The nuptial chamber is prepared with a few sweeps of the tail. Gently drawn towards him, the Scorpioness enters in the wake of her guide.

I visit them a couple of hours later, thinking that I've given them time enough to finish their preparations. I lift the potsherd. They are there in the same posture, face to face and hand in hand. I shall see no more today.

The next day, nothing new either. Each sits confronting the other, meditatively. Without stirring a limb, the gossips, holding each other by the finger-tips, continue their endless interview under the tile. In the evening, at sunset, after sitting linked together for four-and-twenty hours, the couple separate. He goes away from the tile, she remains; and matters have not advanced by an inch.

This observation gives us two facts to remember. After the stroll to celebrate the betrothal, the couple need the mystery and quiet of a shelter. Never would the nuptials be consummated in the open air, amid the bustling crowd, in sight of all. Remove the roof of the house, by night or day, with all possible discretion; and the husband and wife, who seem absorbed in meditation, march off in search of another spot. Also, the sojourn under the cover of a stone is a long one; we have just seen it spun out to twenty-four hours and even then without a decisive result.

12th May.   What will this evening's sitting teach us? The weather is calm and hot, favorable to nocturnal pastimes.

A couple has been formed; how things began I do not know. This time the male is greatly inferior to his corpulent mate. Nevertheless, the skinny wight performs his duty gallantly. Walking backwards, according to rule, with his tail rolled trumpetwise, he marches the fat Scorpioness around the glass ramparts. After one circuit follows another, sometimes in the same, sometimes in the opposite direction.

Pauses are frequent. Then the foreheads touch, bend a little to left and right, as if the two were whispering in each other's ears. The little fore-legs flutter in feverish caresses. What are they saying to each other? How shall we translate their silent epithalamium into words?

The whole household turns out to see this curious team, which our presence in no way disturbs. The pair are pronounced to be "pretty"; and the expression is not exaggerated. Semi-translucent and shining in the light of the lantern, they seem carved out of a block of amber. Their arms outstretched, their tails rolled into graceful spirals, they wander on with a slow movement and with measured tread.

Nothing puts them out. Should some vagabond, taking the evening air and keeping to the wall like themselves, meet them on their way, he stands aside—for he understands these delicate matters—and leaves them a free passage. Lastly, the shelter of a tile receives the strolling pair, the male entering first and backwards: that goes without saying. It is nine o'clock.

The idyll of the evening is followed, during the night, by a hideous tragedy. Next morning, we find the Scorpioness under the potsherd of the previous day. The little male is by her side, but slain, and more or less devoured. He lacks the head, a claw, a pair of legs. I place the corpse in the open, on the threshold of the home. All day long, the recluse does not touch it. When night returns, she goes out and, meeting the deceased on her passage, carries him off to a distance to give him a decent funeral, that is to finish eating him.

This act of cannibalism agrees with what the open-air colony showed me last year. From time to time, I would find, under the stones, a pot-bellied female making a com-

fortable ritual meal off her companion of the night. I
suspected that the male, if he did not break loose in time,
once his functions were fulfilled, was devoured, wholly or
partly, according to the matron's appetite. I now have the
certain proof before my eyes. Yesterday, I saw the couple
enter their home after their usual preliminary, the stroll;
and, this morning, under the same tile, at the moment of my
visit, the bride is consuming her mate.

Well, one supposes that the poor wretch has attained
his ends. Were he still necessary to the race, he would not
be eaten yet. The couple before us have therefore been
quick about the business, whereas, I see that others fail to
finish after provocations and contemplations exceeding in
duration the time which it takes the hour hand to go twice
around the clock. Circumstances impossible to state with
precision—the condition of the atmosphere perhaps, the
electric tension, the temperature, the individual ardor of
the couple—to a large extent accelerate or delay the finale
of the pairing; and this constitutes a serious difficulty for
the observer anxious to seize the exact moment whereat
the as yet uncertain function of the combs might be revealed.

14th May. It is certainly not hunger that stirs up my
animals night after night. The quest of food has nothing to
say to their evening rounds. I have served to the busy
crowd a varied bill of fare, selected from that which they
appear to like best. It includes tender morsels in the shape
of young Locusts; small Grasshoppers, fleshier than the
Acridians; moths minus their wings. At a later season, I add
Dragon-flies, a highly-appreciated dish, as is proved by their
equivalent, the full-grown Ant-lion, of whom I used to find
the remnants, the wings, in the Scorpion's cave.

This luxurious game leaves them indifferent; they pay
no attention to it. Amid the hubbub, the Locusts hop, the
Moths beat the ground with the stumps of their wings, the
Dragon-flies quiver; and the Scorpions pass. They tread
them underfoot, they topple them over, they push them
aside with a stroke of the tail; in short, they absolutely refuse
to look at them. They have other business in hand.

Almost all of them skirt the glass wall. Some of them

obstinately attempt to scale it; they hoist themselves on their tails, fall down, try again elsewhere. With their outstretched fists they knock against the pane; they want to get away at all costs. And yet the grounds are large enough, there is room for all; the walks lend themselves to long strolls. . . . No matter: they want to roam afar. If they were free, they would disperse in every direction. Last year, at the same time, the colonists of the enclosure left the village and I never saw them again.

The spring pairing-season forces them to set forth exploring. The shy hermits of yesterday now leave their cells, and go on love's pilgrimage; heedless of food, they go in quest of their kind. Among the stones of their domain there must be choice spots at which meetings take place, at which assemblies are held. If I were not afraid of breaking my legs, at night, over the rocky obstacles of their hills, I should love to assist at their matrimonial festivals, amid the delights of liberty. What do they do up there, on their bare slopes? Much the same, apparently, as in the glass enclosure. Having picked a bride, they take her about, for a long stretch of time, hand in hand, through the tufts of lavender. If they miss the attractions of my lantern, they have the moon, that incomparable lamp, to light them.

20th May. The sight of the first invitation to a stroll is not an event upon which we can count every evening. Several emerge from under their stones already linked in couples. In this concatenation of clasped fingers, they have passed the whole day, motionless, face to face, meditating. When night comes, without separating for a moment, they resume the walk around the glass begun on the evening before, or even earlier. No one knows when or how the junction was effected. Others meet unexpectedly in sequestered passages, difficult of inspection. By the time that I see them, it is too late: the team is on the way.

Today, chance favors me. The acquaintance is made before my eyes, in the full light of the lantern. A frisky, sprightly male, in his hurried rush through the crowd, suddenly finds himself confronting a fair passer-by who takes his fancy. She does not gainsay him; and things move quickly.

The foreheads touch, the claws engage; the tails swing with a spacious gesture: they stand up vertically, hook together at the tips and softly stroke each other with a slow caress. The two animals stand on their heads in the manner already described. Soon, the raised bodies sink to the ground; fingers are clasped and the couple start on their stroll without more ado. The pyramidal pose, therefore, is really the prelude to the harnessing. The pose, it is true, is not rare between two individuals of the same sex on the meeting; but it is then less correct and above all, less marked by ceremony. At such times, we find movements of impatience, instead of friendly excitations; the tails strike in lieu of fondling each other.

Let us watch the male, who hurries away backwards, very proud of his conquest. Other females are met, who stand around and look on inquisitively, perhaps enviously. One of them flings herself upon the ravished bride, clasps her with legs and makes an effort to stop the team. The male exhausts himself in attempts to overcome this resistance; in vain he shakes, in vain he pulls: things won't move. Undistressed by the accident, he throws up the game. A neighbor is there, close by. Cutting parley short, this time without any further declaration, he takes her hands and invites her to a stroll. She protests, releases herself and runs away.

From among the group of onlookers, a second is solicited, in the same free and easy manner. She accepts, but there is nothing to tell us that she will not escape from her seducer on the way. But what does the coxcomb care? There are more where she came from! And what does he want, when all is said? The first that comes along!

This first-comer he soon finds, for here he is, leading his conquest by the hand. He passes into the belt of light. Exerting all his strength, he tugs and jerks at the other if she refuses to come, but is gentle in his manner when he obtains a docile obedience. Pauses, sometimes rather prolonged, are frequent.

Then the male indulges in some curious exercises. Bringing his claws, or let us say, his arms towards him and then stretching them out again, he compels the female to make a like alternation of movements. The two of them form a system of jointed rods, like a lazy-tongs, opening and closing their quadrilateral by turns. After this gymnastic exercise, the mechanism contracts and remains stationary.

The foreheads now touch; the two mouths come together with tender effusions. The word "kisses" comes to one's mind to express these caresses. It is not applicable; for head, face, lips, cheeks, all are missing. The animal, lopped off short, as though with the shears, has not even a muzzle. Where we look for a face we are confronted with a dead wall of hideous jaws.

And to the Scorpion this represents the supremely beautiful! With his fore-legs, more delicate, more agile than the others, he pats the horrible mask, which in his eyes is an exquisite little face; voluptuously he nibbles and tickles with his jaws the equally hideous mouth opposite. It is all superb in its tenderness and simplicity. The dove is said to have invented the kiss. But I know that he had a forerunner in the Scorpion.

Dulcinea lets her admirer have his way and remains passive, not without a secret longing to slip off. But how is she to set about it? It is quite easy. The Scorpioness makes a cudgel of her tail and brings it down with a bang upon the wrists of her too-ardent wooer, who there and then lets go. The match is broken off, for the time being. Tomorrow, the sulking-fit will be over and things will resume their course. . . .

June sets in. For fear of a disturbance caused by too brilliant an illumination, I have hitherto kept the lantern hung outside, at some distance from the pane. The insufficient light does not allow me to observe certain details of the manner in which the couple are linked when strolling. Do they both play an active part in the scheme of the clasped hands? Are their fingers mutually interlinked? Or is only one of the pair active; and, if so, which? Let us ascertain exactly; the thing is not without importance.

I place the lantern inside, in the center of the cage.

There is good light everywhere. Far from being scared, the Scorpions are gayer than ever. They come hurrying round the beacon; some even try to climb up, so as to be nearer the flame. They succeed in doing so by means of the framework containing the glass panes. They hang on to the edges of the tin strips and stubbornly, heedless of slipping, end by reaching the top. There, motionless, lying partly on the glass, partly on the support of the metal casing, they gaze the whole evening long, fascinated by the burning wick. They remind me of the Great Peacock Moths that used to hang in ecstasy under the reflector of my lamp.

At the foot of the beacon, in the full light, a couple lose no time in standing on their heads. The two fence prettily with their tails and then go a-strolling. The male alone acts. With the two fingers of each claw, he has seized the two fingers of the corresponding claw of the Scorpioness bundled together. He alone exerts himself and squeezes; he alone is at liberty to break the team when he likes: he has but to open his pincers. The female cannot do this; she is a prisoner, handcuffed by her ravisher.

In rather infrequent cases, one may see even more remarkable things. I have caught the Scorpion dragging his sweetheart along by the two fore-arms; I have seen him pull her by one leg and the tail. She had resisted the advances of the outstretched hand; and the bully, forgetful of all reserve, had thrown her on her side and clawed hold of her at random. The thing is quite clear; we have to do with a regular rape, abduction with violence. Even so did Romulus' youths rape the Sabine women.

The brutal ravisher is singularly persistent in his feats of prowess, when we remember that things end tragically sooner or later. The ritual demands that he shall be eaten after the wedding. What a strange world, in which the victim drags the sacrificer by main force to the altar!

From one evening to the next, I become aware that the more corpulent females in my menagerie hardly ever take part in the sport of the linked team; it is nearly always the young, slim-waisted ones to whom the ardent strollers pay their addresses. They must have sprightly flappers. True, there are moments when they have interviews with the others, accompanied by strokes of the tail and attempts at harnessing; but these are brief displays, devoid of any great fervor. No sooner is he seized by the fingers than the portly temptress, with a blow of her tail, rebukes the untimely familiarity. The rejected suitor retires from the contest without insisting further. They go their several ways.

The big-bellied ones are therefore elderly matrons, indifferent nowadays to the effusive manners of the pairing-season. This time last year and perhaps even before, they had their own good spell; and that is enough for them henceforth. The female Scorpion's period of gestation is consequently extraordinarily long, longer than will be often found even among animals of a higher order. It takes her a year or more to mature her germs.

Let us return to the couple whom we have just seen forming up beneath the lantern. I inspect them at six o'clock the next morning. They are under the tile linked precisely as though for a stroll, that is to say, face to face and with clasped fingers. While I watch them, a second pair forms and begins to wander to and fro. The early hour of the expedition surprises me: I had never seen such an incident in broad daylight and was seldom to see it again. As a rule it is at nightfall that the Scorpions go strolling in couples. Whence this hurry today?

I seem to catch a glimpse of the reason. It is stormy weather; in the afternoon, there is incessant, very mild thunder. St. Medard, whose feast fell yesterday, is opening his floodgates wide; it pours all night. The great electric tension and the smell of ozone have stirred up the sleepy hermits, who, nervously irritated, for the most part come to the threshold of their cells, stretching their questioning claws outside and enquiring into the condition of things. Two, more violently excited than the others, have come out, influenced by the intoxication of the pairing which is enhanced by the intoxication of the storm; they suited each other; and here they are solemnly marching to the sound of the thunder-claps.

They pass before open huts and try to go in. The owner

objects. He appears in the doorway, shaking his fists, and his action seems to say:

"Go somewhere else; this place is taken."

They go away. They meet with the same refusal at other doors, the same threats from the occupant. At last, for want of anything better, they make their way under the tile where the first couple have been lodging since the day before. The cohabitation entails no quarrelling; the first settlers and the newcomers, side by side, keep very quiet, each couple absorbed in meditation, completely motionless, with fingers still clasped. And this goes on all day. At five o'clock in the evening, the couples separate. Anxious apparently to take part in the usual twilight rejoicings, the males leave the shelter; the females, on the other hand, remain under the tile. Nothing, so far as I know, has happened during the long interview, nothing despite the stimulating effects of the thunderstorm.

This fourfold occupation of one dwelling is not an isolated instance: groups, regardless of sex, are not infrequent under the potsherds in the glass cage. I have already said that, in their original homes, I have never found two Scorpions under one stone. We must not infer from this that unsociable habits prohibit all intercourse among neighbors; we should be making a mistake: the glazed enclosure tells us so. There are cabins in more than sufficient numbers; each Scorpion would be able to choose himself a dwelling and thenceforth to occupy it as the jealous owner. Nothing of the kind takes place. Once the nocturnal excitement sets in, there is no such thing as a home respected by others. Everything is common property. Whoever wishes to slip under the first tile that offers does so without protest from the occupant. The Scorpions go abroad, walk about and enter any house they may chance upon. In this way, when the twilight diversions are over, groups of three, four, or sometimes more are formed without distinction of sex and, packed pretty closely in the narrow home, spend the rest of the night and the whole of the following day together. For that matter, theirs is only a temporary shanty, which is exchanged next evening for another, according to the strollers' fancy. And these roving gipsies live quite peaceably. There is never any serious strife between them, even when they are five or six in the same messroom.

Now this tolerance prevails only in the adults, due, no doubt, to some degree, to the fear of reprisals. There is another and more imperative reason for peaceful relations: concord is a necessity in assemblies at which the future is being prepared. The Scorpions' characters therefore become assuaged, but not entirely: there are always perverse appetites among the females who are about to enter upon the period of gestation.

I have always present in my mind the memory of the following odious spectacle. A heedless male, who has attained hardly a third or a fourth of his final size, is passing, unthinking of evil, before the door of a dwelling. The fat matron comes out, accosts the poor wretch, picks him up in her claws, kills him with her sting and then quietly eats him.

Scorpion lads and lasses, the one sooner, the other later, perish in the same manner in the glass cage. I scruple to replace the deceased: it would be providing fresh food for the slaughter. There were a dozen of them; and in a few days I have not one left. Without the excuse of hunger, for the regular victuals are plentiful, the females have devoured them all. Youth is certainly a beautiful thing, but it has terrible drawbacks in the society of these ogresses.

I would gladly ascribe these massacres to the peculiar cravings often provoked by pregnancy. The future mother is suspicious and intolerant; to her everything is an enemy, to be got rid of by eating it, when strength permits. And indeed, when the quickly emancipated family is born, in the middle of August, a profound peace reigns in the menagerie. My vigilance is unable to surprise a single case of these outbreaks of cannibalism which used to occur so often.

On the other hand, the males, indifferent to the safety of the family, know nothing of these tragic frenzies. They are peaceful creatures, blunt in their manners, but in any event incapable of ripping up their fellows. We never see two rivals disputing in mortal combat, for the possession of the coveted bride. Things happen, if not mildly, at least without blows of the dagger.

Two suitors come upon the same Scorpioness. Which of the two will propose to her and take her for a walk? The point will be decided by strength of wrist.

Each takes the beauty by the hand nearest to him with the fingers of one claw. One standing on the right, the other on the left, they pull with all their might in opposite directions. The legs, braced backwards, exert a powerful leverage; the flanks quiver; the tails sway to and fro and suddenly dart forward. Now for it! They tug at the Scorpioness by fits and starts with sudden backward runs; it is as though they meant to pull her in two and each to carry off a piece. A declaration of love implies a threat to rend her asunder.

On the other hand, there is no direct exchange of fisticuffs between them, not even a back-hander with the tail. Only the victim is ill-treated and roughly at that. To see these lunatics struggling, you would think that their arms would be torn out. Nevertheless, there are no dislocations.

Weary of an ineffectual contest, the two competitors at last take each other by the hands that remain at liberty: they form a chain of three and resume the process of jerking and tugging more violently than ever. Each of them bustles to and fro, advances, recoils and pulls his hardest till he is exhausted. Suddenly, the more fatigued of the two throws up the sponge and runs away, leaving his adversary in possession of the object of their passions so vehemently disputed. Then, with his free claw, the victor completes the team and the stroll begins. As for the vanquished, we will not trouble about him: he will soon have found something in the crowd to make amends for his confusion.

I will give you another instance of these meek encounters between rivals. A couple are walking along. The male is of medium size, but nevertheless very eager at the game. When his companion refuses to advance, he pulls at her with jerks which send shudders along his spine. A second male, larger than the first, appears upon the scene. The lady takes his fancy; he desires her. Will he abuse his strength, fling himself on the little chap, beat him, perhaps stab him? By no means. Among Scorpions these delicate matters are not decided by force of arms.

The burly fellow leaves the dwarf alone. He goes straight to the coveted fair and seizes her by the tail. Then the two vie with each other in pulling, one in front, the other behind. A brief contest follows, leaving each of them the master of a claw. With frantic violence, one works on the right, the other on the left, as though they wished to pull the dame to pieces. At length the smaller realizes that he is beaten; he lets go and makes off. The big one lays hold of the abandoned prey; and the team takes the road without further incident.

Despite Charles Darwin's estimate of Fabre's powers of observation as "incomparable," he himself was an observer of equal or greater ability. Although a modest man, he once stated, "I think I am superior to the common run of men in noticing things which easily escape attention, and in observing them carefully. My industry has been nearly as great as it could have been in the observation and collection of facts." As a scientist, he was incomparably greater than his French contemporary. What then was the difference between them? One word in a statement by his son Francis supplies the answer: He had "that supreme power of seeing and thinking what most of the world had overlooked." Darwin was primarily interested not in facts but in solutions. Every observation was part of a mosaic constructed to find the answer to a problem, and the problem he chose was of supreme importance.

For Darwin, as for any scientist of stature, observation was one step in the infinitely more complex process of creative understanding. Something of this complexity is indicated in the following article by Douglas Johnson. It illuminates the ways in which observation can be put to use and the errors which may creep in if the most rigorous thinking is not employed. It is also an example of a situation that has occurred time and again in the history of science. Despite the most care-

ful analysis, a problem may remain unsolved because the evidence is incomplete or the correct hypothesis unavailable. Interestingly, there is a strong parallel between Johnson's problem and that which astronomers face in explaining the origin of the craters on the moon.

Douglas Johnson, geologist and geographer, was born in 1878. He was professor of physiography at Harvard until he went to Columbia in 1919. He made an extensive investigation of shoreline changes on the Atlantic Coast and recorded his findings in Shore Processes and Shoreline Development. During World War I, he studied the importance of terrain in the strategy and tactics of warfare. He died in 1944.

MYSTERIOUS CRATERS OF THE CAROLINA COAST

A STUDY IN METHODS OF RESEARCH

DOUGLAS JOHNSON

THE FLAT COASTAL PLAIN of South Carolina and portions of adjacent states is pitted with a vast number of curious oval craters. These depressions vary in longest diameter from a few hundred yards to two or three miles, are partially surrounded by rims of fine-grained sand, and usually have marshes or peat bogs on their floors. Both sandy rims and marshy floors are commonly covered by pine forest, and the traveler could easily pass close to scores of the craters without recognizing their existence. To the natives the oval craters are known as "bays," a name possibly derived from the bay tree frequently found growing in the depressions.

To the geologist, and particularly to one interested in methods of research, these forms have a double interest. The question of their origin presents a peculiarly intriguing problem, one that has attracted the attention of several investigators with diverse results. And the solution of that problem affords an exceptional opportunity to test the value of different methods of prosecuting research. In the space at my disposal I propose to deal simultaneously with both aspects of the "bays problem," but with primary emphasis upon the question of method.

In developing the discussion it will be most convenient to ignore the actual sequence of steps followed in studies carried out in the field, and to adopt a logical rather than a chronological order of presenting evidence, arguments, and conclusions. In fact, I can best set before the reader those considerations respecting methods of research which seem to me of paramount importance if I completely transform the actual study into an imaginary study. I shall, therefore, take the reader with me on an imaginary excursion into the realms of scientific investigation, promising not to burden him with too many technical terms, but to hold the discussion within bounds of ordinary experience and common-sense reasoning.

One warning, however, is necessary. Since this is to be an imaginary investigation of the Carolina craters, I shall repeatedly represent as my own certain field studies made by other workers, and certain conclusions reached by other students of the problem. In doing this I have a double purpose: first, to simplify the study by concentrating attention on one thing only—methods of research; and second, to be in position to criticize methods whenever desirable without appearing to criticize individuals.

FIRST STEP: *Observation and Inference*

The simplest and most direct approach to the solution of a scientific problem is to observe the facts, and then draw the appropriate inferences from them. Where the facts are clear and their explanation obvious, this method may give trustworthy results. In the case of the Carolina "bays" let us imagine that I observed the following pertinent facts, and drew from them the inferences recorded below:

Each bay or crater is oval, as if produced by some object striking the earth obliquely and scooping out an elongated depression. The long axes of the oval depressions are almost if not completely parallel, and trend uniformly from northwest to southeast, as though a great shower of large objects coming from the same direction had produced the tens of thousands of craters actually observed in the field and on aerial photographs of the Carolina coastal plain. There is usually a ridge of sand or sandy rim around each crater, commonly most strongly developed about the southeasterly half of the crater as though an object coming from the northwest had pushed most of the excavated debris toward the southeast. Some craters have double or even triple rims of sand, as if two or three objects had struck nearly in the same spot, throwing up concentric sandy ridges.

These facts and inferences lead almost inevitably to a single simple interpretation, apparently competent to explain all the facts observed—a great cluster of giant meteorites moving from northwest to southeast and striking the earth at an oblique angle scooped out the numerous oval craters and piled up debris, chiefly about their southeastern ends. Where two or three meteorites struck close to the same spot double or triple rims of debris were formed.

Fortunately I discover in the field another group of facts which enables me to fix approximately the period at which the cluster of meteorites struck the earth. Some of the oval craters occur in association with long, nearly straight or but slightly curved ridges of sand of a type found wherever the sea has been receding from a land area but building beaches as it retreats. The characteristics of such beach ridges are so peculiar and so well known to students of shore forms that no competent investigator is likely to confuse them with other phenomena. In the present case I observe that where oval craters are found in association with the beach ridges the craters are often irregularly formed, and the encircling rims poorly developed or wholly lacking. From this I infer that the craters are older than the beach ridges, and that some of the meteorites struck offshore, forming craters on the shallow sea bottom, which were later partly destroyed during the building of beach ridges by wave action.

As many of the craters are very perfect in form and show little evidence of alteration, the fall of the shower of meteorites must have occurred at a comparatively recent period as the geologist reckons time. But since the craters are older than the beach ridges, we must allow sufficient time since the meteoritic shower for waves to build a succession of ridges covering a belt some miles in breadth. I conclude that the shower may have occurred some thousands, possibly some tens of thousands of years ago, but certainly not before the latter part of the glacial period.

Thus I have solved the origin and age of the Carolina craters by a method as simple as it is direct. Were you to ask me to tell just what this method is, I might respond in either of two ways. I might say that it is just the good old-fashioned, common-sense method of observing the pertinent facts and then deciding how they were caused. Were I inclined to be more technical I would say that it is the *inductive method,* according to which the investigator is led directly and almost unconsciously from the observed facts to their more or less obvious explanation. When a problem is simple, the facts clear, and their explanation obvious, the inductive method may give good results.

SECOND STEP: *Checking Conclusions*

If I am a careful investigator I will not accept my own conclusion without attempting to check its validity. In scientific research one of the commonest methods of making such a check is to determine what consequences, previously unconsidered, ought to follow if the conclusion be correct. Should further study show that these anticipated consequences actually do occur, confidence in the conclusion will be powerfully confirmed.

This so-called *deductive method* of research supplements admirably the inductive method previously described. The conclusion reached by the direct or inductive method is not to be too hastily accepted, but is treated merely as an hypothesis to be tested, a "working hypothesis" to serve as the basis for further study. From this working hypothesis the investigator "deduces" the consequences which logically ought to follow in case the hypothesis be valid, and then ascertains whether the deduced consequences are really matched by facts previously observed or newly discovered as a result of further search. A close correspondence between deduced consequences and observed facts inevitably gives the investigator added confidence in his interpretation.

In my study of the Carolina craters I proceed to apply the deductive method. If it be true that the craters were produced by a great shower of giant meteorites coming from the northwest and striking the Carolina coastal plain at an oblique angle, it should logically follow that the area of abundant craters corresponds with an area of abundant "finds" of meteorites as reported by collectors of these visitors from outer space. Examination of maps showing the distribution of known meteorite finds, published in Nininger's volume, *Our Stone-Pelted Planet*, reveals the fact that the southeastern United States is an area where meteorites have been most abundantly discovered. An oval encompassing the area of most abundant craters also encompasses the area of most abundant meteorites.

A further logical deduction may be drawn from the hypothesis in question. If meteorites coming from the northwest struck the earth obliquely to form oval craters, they should frequently have penetrated the loose sandy soil of the coastal plain and be now reposing below the surface at or near the southeastern ends of such craters. Since many meteorites contain significant amounts of iron, a magnetometer survey of these southeastern areas should frequently show the presence of "magnetic highs," due to the attractive influence of iron within the buried meteorites. Accordingly I make magnetometer surveys covering the southeastern ends of several bays and adjacent territory. In every instance the surveys show distinct magnetic highs in the areas in question.

I conclude that the explanation of crater origin reached by the inductive method, and strikingly confirmed by two critical tests formulated by the deductive method, is well substantiated. On the face of the record I have made out an excellent case for my hypothesis. If the conclusions are published they will be incorporated into textbooks of geology and astronomy. But I hesitate. Years of experience in scientific research breed in the investigator an attitude of healthy skepticism. He has learned that only too often "things are not what they seem." He knows that methods of research can be seductive as well as deductive or inductive; that the deductive method is not always as conclusive as it appears to be; that despite widespread belief to the contrary, the supposedly simple and safe inductive method may be quite as dangerous as the deductive method. So the moment he distrusts conclusions reached by the simple and direct inductive method, or by the more indirect deductive method, or by both methods combined, the investigator turns to a third method, far more elaborate than the other two, but far more likely to lead him to the correct solution of his problem.

THIRD STEP: *Analysis of Observations and Inferences*

This third method of research is best called the *analytical method*. In plain language it consists in separating into its component parts every step in the investigation; and testing critically the validity of each and every part. While one half of the mind, the creative half, searches out and brings together the bricks, the mortar, and the timbers of evidence and argument, and builds these into a complete and satisfying theory, the judicial half of the mind stands jealously by, subjecting to impartial but relentless scrutiny the quality of every brick, the cementing power of every bit of mortar, and the soundness of every timber that goes into the final structure. In the very nature of the case such a process cannot be as direct and rapid as the inductive method by which my meteoritic hypothesis was reached. Nor is it even as simple as the deductive method by which that hypothesis was tested. It is, indeed, far more elaborate than either of these, a complicated, even a cumbersome, method if you please. But it has merits possessed by neither of the other two.

In the first place it makes use of both induction and deduction far more extensively than do the simpler methods which bear those names. As we shall see, not one interpretation but several are treated both inductively and deductively, thus multiplying whatever advantages may lie in those procedures.

In the second place, the new method brings into play the analytical powers of the mind to an extent impossible in either the inductive or the deductive method. It is this outstanding peculiarity which causes the third method to be known as the "analytical method." And it is the dominating role played by analysis in this method which makes it more likely than any other to discover hidden weaknesses in a hypothesis or theory under investigation.

In the third place, the analytical method involves a conscious effort of the mind to invent and test all possible explanations of a given phenomenon or group of phenomena, thus greatly enhancing the probability that the correct explanation will be discovered. It is this invention and testing of more than one tentative explanation or hypothesis which causes the method to be frequently called the "method of multiple-working hypotheses."

In the fourth place, the analytical method, by its employment of multiple hypotheses, naturally paves the way to discovery that a given phenomenon or group of phenomena is the product of several agencies acting in conjunction or in succession. The true solution of a problem has often remained long hidden because the investigator assumed that the explanation was single and simple, when in reality it was multiple and complex.

Finally, the analytical method possesses the enormous advantage of constantly directing the mind toward new facts and new lines of argument, this being an inevitable and valuable consequence of the effort to test a variety of diverse hypotheses. Under such circumstances the chances that significant facts will escape the eye, or important lines of reasoning escape the mind, are greatly diminished.

Let us now attack the problem of the Carolina craters

anew, placing dependence this time on the more complex but more trustworthy analytical method. I first go back to my initial step, and subject the original observations to critical analysis.

I stated that the craters are oval, and so they appeared to be. But more critical scrutiny reveals the existence of systematic departures from the simple oval form. The northeastern sides of the bays are prevailingly more strongly curved than the southwestern sides. It is difficult to see why plunging meteorites should produce craters which are systematically asymmetrical.

Further scrutiny shows that many of the craters are pear-shaped rather than oval, with the narrower end always directed toward the southeast. It is conceivable that an obliquely plunging meteorite might produce a narrow groove where it first touches the earth, and a broader depression where the full body enters; but in that event the narrow ends of the craters should point toward the northwest.

Parallelism of the northwest-southeast axes of the elongated craters appeared to be one of their most remarkable characteristics. But careful measurements reveal the fact that there are many divergences in axial direction, amounting to more than 50° in some instances, to 80° in a few. It is difficult to understand how meteorites could maintain uniformity of direction for long distances through space to arrive as a cluster, then suddenly to diverge so widely as these angles indicate. Disruptive explosion shortly before striking the earth offers a partial but not wholly satisfying explanation.

It was stated that rims of sand were most strongly developed about the southeastern ends of the craters. Here again my observation was defective. Critical study of more than a hundred craters on the ground and of a far larger number in aerial photographs proves conclusively that the locus of major accumulation is about the *southeast quadrant* of the craters, rather than about the southeastern half. In other words, there is prevailingly a marked asymmetry in the distribution of the sandy rims. It is difficult to see why a plunging meteorite should push up more debris on the southeastern side of a crater than on the southwestern side.

I pointed out that some craters have double or triple rims. Here observation was incomplete. Further examination reveals that some craters have as many as six or eight rims. A further significant fact is revealed: while the successive rims are nearly concentric, they converge and ultimately merge before reaching the northwestern ends of the craters. About the northwestern ends there are seldom if ever multiple rims, and frequently no rims at all. It is scarcely conceivable that as many as six or eight successive meteorites should strike almost exactly in the same spot, yet with a systematic slight displacement toward the northwest to give rims so peculiarly arranged as those observed.

I noted that some of the craters associated with beach ridges were irregular in form, and that their rims were incomplete or missing; and it was concluded that the craters must have been formed before the beach ridges were developed. Analysis shows that in this case both observation and reasoning were defective. Beach ridges as well as craters are in places poorly developed or wholly absent. Critical study shows that beach ridges never continue unbroken and well developed through a poorly outlined crater; but that perfectly formed craters repeatedly interrupt the sequence of ridges. The conclusion seems inescapable that the craters, not the beach ridges, were formed last. Further observation shows that craters are often arranged in chains, like oblong beads strung obliquely on a thread, and conforming perfectly to the trend of the beach ridges. It is difficult to believe that falling meteorites could so perfectly adjust their points of impact to a pre-existing topography.

Thus critical analysis of the very first stage of our investigation places the problem in a wholly new light. It shows how faulty were my initial observations, and hence how untrustworthy were the inferences based on those observations. Grave doubt is thrown on the validity of the conclusion reached by the inductive method of study.

FOURTH STEP: *Analysis of the Deductive Tests*

But what about the deductive portion of the study, and the strong support this testing process brought to the meteoritic hypothesis of crater origin? To answer this question the deductive study must now be subjected to critical analysis.

It was pointed out that if the meteoritic hypothesis were correct the area of abundant craters and the area of abundant meteorites should correspond; and it was shown that both craters and meteorites are most numerous in an oval area in the southeastern United States. But analysis is inquisitive. It is not satisfied with a vague oval encompassing a vast area. It asks for a more precise map of the distribution of abundant craters, for a similar map showing the distribution of abundant meteorite finds, and for a critical comparison of these two maps. When this is forthcoming it is discovered that the area of bays and the area of meteorites are mutually exclusive, save for a very limited overlapping near Columbia, South Carolina. It develops further that in not a single instance has a meteorite ever been found in or near one of the craters, whereas in true meteorite craters such association is common. In the glaring light of analysis one supposedly strong confirmation of the meteoritic hypothesis disappears like the mists of the morning.

Next I turn the light of analysis upon the magnetometer survey which seemingly gave another strong confirmation of the meteoritic interpretation of crater origin. Immediately I note a defect in my method of conducting the surveys. Instead of selecting a typical area containing a number of craters and surveying that entire area, I conducted limited surveys about the southeastern ends of selected craters. This seemed necessary in the interests of economy of time and money. But it jeopardized the intended test of the hypothesis, since if for any reason there were numerous deposits of iron below the surface throughout the region, one would be pretty sure to get one or more magnetic highs somewhere in the vicinity of the southeastern end of almost any crater. So long as my surveys were restricted to the southeastern ends of craters the evidence of the magnetic highs would seem very convincing. Only in case the surveys were extended over a large area, revealing magnetic highs in many other positions, would the inconclusive character of the evidence become apparent.

In the light of this analysis I begin to extend the partial surveys over broader areas. Then I discover that the magnetic highs do occur beyond the areas previously mapped. I find, further, that some of them are beginning to show marked elongation in a northeast-southwest direction. I recall that this is the trend of Appalachian structures in older rocks known to be buried beneath those coastal plain beds in which the craters occur. I know that the coastal plain is a wedge-shaped deposit with its thin edge toward the interior, barely covering the older rocks near the thin inner edge but deeply burying them near the coast line. So my reasoning runs that if the magnetic highs of my surveys are due to iron in the older rocks they should be very strongly developed in surveys made near the inner edge of the coastal plain, but scarcely perceptible in surveys made along the coast. Test surveys about craters in both areas give strong highs in the interior, faint highs near the sea. The necessary conclusion is that the magnetic highs are caused by iron in the older rocks, and not by iron in buried meteorites. What was apparently the strongest support of the meteoritic hypothesis vanishes under the searching light of analysis.

The analytical method must be applied not only to observations and the inferences drawn from them, and to deductive tests of those inferences, but also to any assumptions that may underlie the inferences. There is one basic assumption underlying the whole discussion of the meteoritic hypothesis which has thus far gone unchallenged. This is the assumption that meteorites striking the earth obliquely will excavate elongated, more or less oval depressions. Let us now analyze this assumption.

Tests made with guns firing large and small projectiles show that a swiftly moving projectile striking the earth obliquely may act in several different ways: *a*] it may penetrate the ground in the oblique direction of incidence;

b] if the angle of incidence is too low, it may strike the surface a glancing blow and pass off into space again;   c] it may explode upon impact. In the first instance the crater produced will depart but slightly from the circular form. An angle of impact sufficiently low to produce a greatly elongated crater will not permit penetration. The glancing blow resulting from low-angle impact produces an elongated crater due to the ploughing action of the projectile. In both instances the breadth of the crater is not much greater than the diameter of the projectile. This means that to produce the Carolina craters by simple penetration or by ploughing we must invoke the aid of truly gigantic meteorites having diameters measured in thousands of feet, six to eight thousand or more in some cases. The largest meteorites known to have reached the earth measure less than a score of feet in maximum diameter.

A small projectile may by violent explosion produce a large crater. It is conceivable that a moderately large meteorite by exploding on impact, or by causing either moisture in the ground or the rock material to volatilize with explosive effect, might produce a much larger crater. But explosion craters are circular in outline regardless of the angle at which the projectile strikes the earth. In the World War it was found impossible to determine from an explosion crater the direction from which the enemy's gun fired a shell. All known meteorite craters are approximately circular. Elongated forms occur only when there is evidence suggesting that two meteorites struck close together.

Thus the advocate of the meteoritic hypothesis finds himself between the two horns of a dilemma. To get elongated craters he must invoke meteorites of utterly unheard-of proportions. To get large craters from smaller meteorites he must invoke explosive impact, which is incompetent to produce elongated craters like those observed.

FIFTH STEP: *Invention and Analysis of Multiple Hypotheses*

Analysis has by now abundantly demonstrated that a major

error was made in my method of attacking the problem of the Carolina craters. I assumed that the problem was a simple one, easily solved by the simple and direct method of induction, supplemented by the fairly simple but indirect method of deduction. Analysis has convinced me that the problem is far more difficult and complicated than at first supposed, and that its solution can safely be attempted only with the aid of the somewhat cumbersome but far more dependable analytical method, involving the invention of multiple hypotheses and the critical use of analysis during every stage of the procedure.

My next step in prosecuting the study is to analyze further the facts observed, with a view to discovering whether the problem is really a unit, or a series of problems not subject to any one simple explanation. It is first noted that there is the problem of the crater-like depressions, and I deliberately invent as many hypotheses as possible to explain them: *a*] solution sinkholes resulting from local removal of soluble rock such as limestone, marl, gypsum, phosphate rock, rock salt, arkosic sandstone; *b*] "blowouts" due to erosive action of the wind; *c*] local removal of sand by upwelling springs fed by water under artesian pressure; and so on. I also retain *d*] the hypothesis of excavation by impact of meteorites, since the fact that this hypothesis was supported by invalid evidence and arguments does not necessarily prove that the hypothesis itself is invalid.

Second I note that the *shape* of the depressions may be a problem entirely distinct from their original creation. Accordingly I invent as many hypotheses as I can to account for their shape, among them the following: *a*] erosion by waves on lakes occupying the depressions to give their smoothly curving inner margins; *b*] attack by waves driven by storm winds from the northwest or southeast to explain elongation of the craters in that general direction; *c*] more wave attack from the southwest than from the northeast to account for the greater bulging and sharper curvature of the northeastern sides of the craters; *d*] slumping of water-saturated sand into ever-enlarging, artesian-spring basins to give circular depressions which would then be elongated in a northwesterly direction by migration of the springs "headward" or up the coastal plain slope.

In the third place it is noted that the sandy rims may be divided into two groups. 1] those found wholly outside the depressions, often irregular in shape; and 2] more regularly formed ridges which seem to lie within the contours of the craters. As hypotheses of origin for the outer and often irregular rims I entertain a] the possibility that they were thrown out by meteoritic ploughing or explosion; b] that they are ridges of dune sand blown out of the depressions by winds. For the inner and usually very regular rims there is a] the possibility of a wind-blown origin; b] also the possibility that they are beach ridges built by wave action when lakes occupied the craters, their convergence and disappearance toward the northwest being tentatively ascribed to progressive elongation of the lake in that direction due to headward migration of artesian springs or some other cause.

Thus a large number of working hypotheses are quickly accumulated, some of which it is hoped will contain enough of the truth to direct me toward the correct interpretation. To discover these grains of truth, to develop them fully, and to follow them to a successful solution of the mystery of crater origin is a long and complicated process. Every one of the many working hypotheses must be fully elaborated, its logical consequences deduced, the deduced consequences compared with facts already observed or newly discovered by additional search, invalid hypotheses rejected and faulty hypotheses revised, while at every step of the procedure the searchlight of analysis is constantly directed upon each bit of evidence and each line of argument, in the hope of revealing some weakness hitherto concealed. The hypothesis which survives so drastic a scrutiny does not necessarily represent the correct conclusion. But it is far more likely to be correct than is a conclusion reached by the simple inductive method, the deductive method, or by both combined.

Obviously it would be quite impossible in limited space to present in full all the stages of so complex a process as the analytical study of the Carolina craters. Furthermore, it is

not profitable for the investigator to elaborate for others all
the excursions, many of them fruitless, he was compelled
to make in the course of a given research. I shall, however,
present briefly a few of the most interesting deductions developed in the course of my analysis, and the observed
facts which seemed to match those deductions so closely
as to justify the ultimate conclusion that the mysterious
craters of the Carolina coast have, in fact, a complex rather
than a simple origin.

SIXTH STEP: *Deductive Testing of Multiple Hypotheses*

If the craters are solution sinkholes there should be some
correlation between distribution of the craters and the distribution of known soluble rock. Furthermore, sinkholes of
all sizes, down to those measuring but a few feet across,
should be associated with the larger craters; and some at
least should show the steep, clifflike walls found in many
sinkholes. Investigation shows that in some localities crater
distribution is coincident with the known extension of
moderately soluble arkosic sands or more soluble limestone
or marl. Elsewhere such correlation is less clear. Where
very soluble rock is present the craters are associated with
typical sinkholes of all sizes, often in great numbers; and
both craters and smaller sinks show steep inner walls, sometimes thirty feet or more in height, a feature which escaped
observation until analysis directed search for the pertinent
facts. Whatever the cause of the craters, it seems a reasonable inference that the process of crater formation sometimes involved solution of the country rock, with consequent
development of typical sinkhole features.

If the craters were excavated in loose sand or loam by
springs welling up from below under artesian pressure, loose
sand or loam should be found at the surface in areas where
the craters are abundant. We should also find that the
geological conditions are favorable to the widespread development of artesian water, and it would seem reasonable
to expect that some of the artesian springs might still be

operating at the present time. Field examination long ago showed that the surface formation of the coastal plain is almost everywhere a loose sand, usually white or buff in color. The bays are most commonly excavated in this sand, or in a sandy loam immediately underlying it. It has also long been known that the Atlantic Coastal Plain offers highly favorable conditions for the development of artesian water supplies, some of the artesian horizons lying close to the surface and giving birth to artesian springs which well up through the overlying sand or sandy loam. Many of these springs are still functioning, and are known to the natives as "fountain springs" or "boiling springs" because of the force with which the water rushes up into the bottoms of the spring basins. Some of the springs are found in major craters, others in minor depressions. All these facts were known to geologists years ago; but their possible relation to the problem of crater origin was not suspected until that problem was recently attacked by the analytical method.

It is only reasonable to suppose that when the coastal plain was first raised above sea level, and before rivers cutting into the plain offered lower outlets for underground waters, there must have been countless such springs bubbling up through the sandy soil. As the sand must then have been saturated with water it would slump or flow into the ever-enlarging basins, producing circular craters in case the position of the springs remained fixed. But since the coastal plain slopes southeast, and underground waters must then have moved southeastward down the slope, springs would normally migrate "headward" or upcurrent, just as a waterfall in a river migrates upstream. Such migration should transform circular spring basins or craters into more or less oval craters. Where headward migrating springs increased in volume of outflow as solution enlarged their underground channels, excavation should become more effective and the basins should increase in diameter with the passage of time, thus producing pear-shaped craters with the narrower ends directed toward the southeast.

In either case the long axes of the craters should be

parallel to the direction of underground-water movement. This would normally be from northwest to southeast; but local conditions might in places deflect the ground-water currents, and hence give craters with long axes diverging notably from the usual down-slope direction. Thus past geological conditions, not considered until the analytical method was applied to the problem of crater origin, appear to explain at one stroke the major forms of the craters, the prevailing northwest-southeast orientation of their axes, and the occasional marked deviations from that prevailing direction.

Upwelling waters tend to seek the lowest outlets on the surface. In a series of beach ridges and intervening swales such outlets will normally be in the lower swales. But sometimes these swales are occupied by impervious silts and clays. Under such conditions the easiest route to the surface would be through the porous sands of the broad, relatively flat ridges. In these facts we apparently find explanation of the existence of chains of craters parallel to the trend of the beach-ridge system, the chains sometimes occupying the swales, sometimes occurring on the ridges.

Another legitimate deduction from the artesian spring hypothesis of crater excavation deserves attention. If the craters were excavated by artesian waters welling up from under ground, those waters must have had a means of escape on the surface. In other words, there should have been outlet channels leading from the craters, and those channels should still be visible where spring waters are still flowing, or where they ceased to flow so recently that the channels have not yet been buried by drifting sand or other deposits. Craters produced by scooping or by explosion, and surrounded by rims of the expelled debris, normally do not have outlet channels. So long as the meteoritic hypothesis dominated attention no one sought for outlet channels, and apparently no one noticed their existence. Not until the analytical method was applied to the problem, and one of its multiple hypotheses by requiring their existence directed observation to their discovery, was it learned that outlet channels are one of the characteristic features of the craters.

Some of the channels are still occupied by outflowing spring waters.

The outflowing of water from the craters offers a reasonable explanation for a fact seemingly inexplicable on the basis of the meteoritic hypothesis. Calculations of the amount of sand found in the ridges or rims surrounding the craters show that the total is insignificant compared to the vast bulk of material removed to form the basins of the craters. This fact, seemingly fatal to the meteoritic hypothesis, is readily explained if during the whole period of crater development outflowing waters were busy transporting seaward the silt and fine sand composing part of the original coastal plain deposit.

The hypothesis that lakes occupied the craters opens the way to explain certain of their features quite independently of their original formation. One characteristic of the depressions is the remarkable simplicity or smoothness of their inner contours. Slumping of saturated sand might give roughly circular or ovoid basins, but it is difficult to believe that this process alone would produce such smooth outlines as are actually observed. It is known, however, that waves tend to simplify shorelines by eroding projecting angles and filling re-entrants. If the basins were occupied by lakes it seems inevitable that their inner contours must have been regularized by wave erosion and wave deposition.

But while waves tend to smooth out the irregularities of a shore, dominant wave action from one direction may erode one side of a lake more than another. It will later appear that in the region of the Carolina bays dominant winds come from the northwest, west, and southwest. Winds from the first direction would tend to drive waves against the southeastern end of the lake; but winds from the west and southwest would both drive waves against the northeastern side of the lake, the maximum effect being felt toward the central portion of that side because there the waves would arrive from the greatest fetch of open and deeper water. The result should be to sharpen the curvature of that side of the crater. We have already noted that such asymmetry of crater outline does exist.

The lake hypothesis makes possible a full explanation of the parallel sandy ridges within the craters. These have all the characteristics of ordinary beach ridges cast up by waves, a fact not noticed by any observer until the analytical method with its systematic use of multiple hypotheses was brought into play. Such ridges are characteristically parallel or nearly so for limited distances, but normally converge toward their extremities. Migration of the lakes toward the northwest, due to spring migration "upcurrent" or up the ground-water slope, would prevent the development of successive beach ridges about the northwestern ends of the craters, where they are in fact normally absent. Gradual lowering of the ground-water level, an inevitable result of the progressive deepening of river valleys in the coastal plain, must have caused a lowering of lake levels. This fully accounts for the fact that we sometimes find as many as six or eight successive and nearly concentric beach ridges, the inner ones progressively lower than the outer ones. Where soluble rocks are involved the ground-water level, and hence the level of near-by lakes, may drop suddenly when new channel ways are opened by solution. This offers a possible explanation of the fact, hitherto overlooked, that in certain closely associated groups of craters there uniformly occurs a break between an upper and a lower beach ridge or set of beach ridges.

Just as the analytical study of the Carolina craters first opened our eyes to the possibility that the craters and their sandy rims might have quite independent modes of origin, so it was the analytical method that first directed attention to the possibility that the sandy rims themselves might belong to two distinct categories of phenomena each having its own peculiar mode of origin. Once the observer had his "out-sight" sharpened by this fuller insight into the nature of his problem, he had no difficulty in distinguishing two types of ridges or rims: one type prevailingly narrow, seldom over two or three feet high, regular in outline, and located within the crater margin; and a second type often of great breadth, from three to fifteen feet or more in height, with exterior borders highly irregular and poorly defined, the whole lying on or outside of the crater rim. As a rule the contrast is not obvious, but critical study seems to establish the reality of the distinction.

It manifestly is not possible to ascribe to wave action those ridges or rims lying outside the crater and sometimes extending one or two thousand feet from what must have been the border of the lake occupying the crater basin. The sand is fairly fine, of uniform grade, and the surface of the deposit often has the undulatory aspect of an accumulation laid down by the wind. Thus the hypothesis that the sandy ridges are wind-blown deposits seems applicable to the outer rims. It may explain in part the inner rims, where these appear to be dune ridges superposed on earlier beach ridges in a manner common along sandy shores. But the aeolian hypothesis (wind) alone fails to explain both the form and the distribution of the inner ridges, while the lacustrine hypothesis (lake) satisfactorily accounts for both. Only when applied to the outer rims does the aeolian hypothesis appear competent. An adequate source of bare, dry sand was provided by the sandy beaches bordering the lakes in the craters.

Analysis suggests two deductive tests which we may apply to the aeolian hypothesis:

a] If the outer rims consist of material brought by the wind, the deposit should contain no material too coarse to be transported by that agency, except such as Indians or other forms of life might have imported. Under the meteoritic hypothesis there should be fragments of underlying rock layers ploughed up by the plunging meteorite or blown up by explosion. Careful study of many rims by different observers has failed to reveal the presence of any rock fragments in the rim, except occasional bits of chert or other similar material believed to have been carried in by Indians. The rims are composed of fine sand identical in character with known dune sands.

b] It is the outer rims which show best the major accumulation of sand about the southeastern quadrants of the craters, a peculiar asymmetry difficult to explain under the meteoritic hypothesis of crater origin. If the outer rims are really of aeolian origin, examination of weather records for the Carolina coastal plain, or for that part of the plain occupied by the craters, should show dominant winds from the opposite quarter. Study of records furnished by the U.S. Weather Bureau shows that throughout the region in question winds of fairly high velocity blow for the greatest number of hours from northwest, west, and southwest. If we plot about an ideal oval bay the rims which would be formed by winds blowing from each of the three directions mentioned, and then combine these into a single master rim, we find that the sand accumulation has its major development about the southeast quadrant of the ideal crater, precisely as it does in nature about the southeast quadrants of the Carolina craters. The hypothesis that the large outer rims are of aeolian origin is thus strongly confirmed.

FINAL STEP: *Conclusion*

In our present discussion it has been shown that the inductive study of an apparently easy and simple problem led us to a solution dramatic in its quality and convincing in its simplicity. Deductive tests of that solution appeared strongly to support its validity. But critical analysis stepped in and revealed hidden weaknesses. Application of the full analytical method, with its invention and testing of multiple hypotheses, led us to conclude that the problem was difficult rather than easy, complex rather than simple, and that a combination of unrelated causes was necessary to account for the facts observed. The meteoritic hypothesis was found wholly incompetent to explain the Carolina craters and their associated features. Evidence was discovered which seemed to indicate that the craters resulted in part from the solution of soluble rock formations and in part from removal of sand by artesian springs; that wave action on lakes within the craters reshaped their shores and built some of their sandy rims; and that wind action built up the major rims partially surrounding the outer margins of the craters. For the simple meteoritic hypothesis it became necessary to substitute the more complex "solution-artesian-lacustrine-aeolian hypothesis."

Whether or not this more complex hypothesis is valid it is too early to say. The case in its favor is stronger than I have represented, since there are lines of supporting evidence which for lack of space cannot be set forth. But the hypothesis has its weaknesses. Headward migration of artesian springs has been assumed, not demonstrated. Excavation of large basins by artesian springs has not been observed, or at least not recognized as such. To some the perfection of form of many bays may appear too remarkable to be fully explained by the processes invoked. I can only say that the explanation offered is the best I have been able to devise, and that to me the forces appealed to seem competent to produce the results observed. But I fully realize that some other hypothesis, perhaps one that wholly escaped my search, may prove the key which will solve the mystery of the Carolina craters.

Be that as it may, some worth-while lessons can be drawn from our study. One is that the simplicity of an explanation is no guarantee of its validity. The human mind prefers simple explanations of natural phenomena. Yet it remains true that Nature often moves in complex as well as in mysterious ways her wonders to perform.

We have seen that the inductive method of research, often championed as safer than the deductive method, can lead us quite as far astray. It is as easy to induce erroneous inferences from observed facts as it is to deduce erroneous consequences from invented hypotheses.

We have demonstrated the value of properly controlled deductive reasoning. Uncritical deductions lent a false color of validity to an erroneous hypothesis. But deductions controlled and tested by critical analysis revealed our mistakes, and paved the way to a fuller understanding of the problem.

We have gained an impression of the dominant role which analysis should play in scientific research. The successful solution of any complex problem will usually depend primarily upon the skillful employment of the analytical powers of the investigator's mind.

Finally, we have had to confess that not even the analytical method can guarantee the investigator success in his search for truth. Had we examined other methods of research, including the experimental method so valuable in the physical sciences, our conclusion must have been the same. There is no royal road to truth, nor does that goddess bear any patent of nobility by which she may be recognized when found. Only too often is the truth of today revealed in tomorrow's light as error in disguise.

This brief section speaks for itself. A note on the author will be found on page 131.

HYPOTHESIS

W. I. B. BEVERIDGE

THE ROLE OF hypothesis in research can be discussed more effectively if we consider examples of discoveries which originated from hypotheses. One of the best illustrations of such a discovery is provided by the story of Christopher Columbus' voyage; it has many of the features of a classic discovery in science. (a) He was obsessed with an idea— that since the world is round he could reach the Orient by sailing west, (b) the idea was by no means original, but evidently he had obtained some additional evidence from a sailor blown off his course who claimed to have reached land in the west and returned, (c) he met great difficulties in getting someone to provide the money to enable him to test his idea as well as in the actual carrying out of the experimental voyage, (d) when finally he succeeded he did not find the expected new route, but instead found a whole new world, (e) despite all evidence to the contrary he clung to the bitter end to his hypothesis and believed that he had found the route to the Orient, (f) he got little credit or reward during his lifetime and neither he nor others realized the full implications of his discovery, (g) since his time evidence has been brought forward showing that he was by no means the first European to reach America.

Perhaps the most famous example of belief in a false hypothesis in the history of science is geocentric astronomy, which was accepted from the earliest times until after the death of Copernicus. To explain observed phenomena, philosophers postulated a series of crystal spheres in which stars and planets were imbedded, and flaws in the theory were accounted for by constantly more complex arrangements. One reason for its overthrow was the relative simplicity with which the heliocentric theory explained the evidence.

James B. Conant here discusses a false hypothesis from the history of chemistry. From our superior vantage point, the weaknesses of the phlogiston theory seem obvious, and we wonder why they were ignored. Actually they were not ignored —the holes were patched. The scientists of the eighteenth century lacked neither intelligence nor inventiveness. They accepted the theory because it explained and synthesized, and because there was nothing to take its place. Einstein once stated that a single piece of contrary evidence could destroy the validity of relativity theory. If past experience is any guide, such evidence would result in a process of tinkering and not in outright abandonment of the theory.

James Bryant Conant is one of America's outstanding scientists and educators. He was born in Massachusetts in 1893 and was educated at Harvard. He became professor of chemistry there in 1927 and president of the university in 1933. During World War II he played an active part in the development of the atomic bomb and in 1953 became United States high

*commissioner for Germany. More recently he has been an
exponent of new methods of general education in primary and
secondary schools.*

THE OVERTHROW OF THE PHLOGISTON THEORY

JAMES B. CONANT

TWO IMPORTANT PRINCIPLES in the Tactics and Strategy
of Science are as follows:

First, a useful concept may be a barrier to the acceptance
of a better one if long-intrenched in the minds of scientists.

Second, experimental discoveries must fit the time; facts
may be at hand for years without their significance being
realized; the total scientific situation must be favorable for
the acceptance of new views.

The case history which illustrates excellently these two
important points might be entitled "the overthrow of the
phlogiston theory" or "Lavoisier's work on combustion in
the 1770's." As indicated by the first phrase the case also
affords a classic example of the mustering of evidence pro
and con when two rival concepts are in collision. This
phenomenon though frequent is usually so transient in the
history of science as to be hard to capture for purposes of
historical study. In the investigation of combustion the
normal progress of science was, so to speak, delayed; this
fact, in a sense, accounts for why a study of this difficult
passage in scientific history is of special significance to those
interested in the Tactics and Strategy of Science.

The easiest way to understand the revolution in chemistry associated with the name of Lavoisier is first to describe
the phenomena in question in terms of modern concepts;
then to show how for nearly a hundred years everyone was

thoroughly confused. This pedagogic device would have to be used by the instructor in the course I am suggesting. It involves the dogmatic statement of a certain amount of popularized physics and chemistry, but I doubt if the presentation would be much more arbitrary in this respect than most freshman courses. Indeed, some of the material might be said to be common knowledge today.

Almost every high-school graduate "knows" (I put quotation marks around the word) that air is primarily a mixture of oxygen gas and nitrogen gas; furthermore, when a candle or a match or a cigarette "burns," heat and light are being evolved by a chemical reaction involving oxygen. This is called "combustion." If we burn enough material in a closed space, the combustion stops because the oxygen is used up. What burns? Some but not all of the students will say that in the cases mentioned it is a group of carbon compounds, and some will add that the products of combustion are carbon dioxide, CO_2 and water, H_2O. Anyone who has an elementary knowledge of chemical symbols usually loves to share the information! Suppose you heat molten tin in air at a high temperature for a long time, and the bright metal becomes covered with a scum, obviously not a metal. What has happened? A combination with oxygen—an oxide is formed —the bright boys and girls answer. Correct. Suppose we heat this nonmetallic substance, an oxide, with carbon. What would happen? The carbon would combine with the oxygen, giving an oxide of carbon and leaving the metal. This is what happens in making iron from iron ore, the very bright boy tells you.

All very simple and plain. And you can set students to work in high-school laboratories to prove it. Yet it is an historic fact that at the time of the American Revolution not one philosopher or experimentalist out of one hundred could have given you an inkling of this explanation which we now designate as "correct." Instead, they would have talked learnedly of "phlogiston," a name probably totally unfamiliar to all but the chemists who read this book. Nearly a hundred years after Newton, and still everyone was thoroughly bewildered by such a simple matter as combustion! This fact needs to be brought home to all who would understand science and who talk of the "scientific method."

The chemical revolution was practically contemporary with the American Revolution and, of course, just preceded the French Revolution. Lavoisier, the man who single-handed, but building on the work of others, made the revolution, lost his head at the hands of the Revolutionary Tribune in 1794 (though he was by no means hostile to the basic aims of the great social and political upheaval). Whether or not he was betrayed by a scientific colleague (Fourcroy) who at least was an ardent supporter of the extreme party then in power, is an intriguing historical question; its study would be a by-product of this case history in which certain students would take great interest. Likewise, the fact that another prominent figure in the final controversy was Priestley, a Unitarian clergyman, who was made an honorary citizen by the French Assembly and then fled to America in the very year of Lavoisier's execution to escape a reactionary English mob, adds zest to the story. There is no lack of material to connect science with society in the late eighteenth century, though the connection I think is more dramatic than significant; at all events, for keeping up students' interest it can hardly be surpassed.

The Classic Experiment on the Role of Oxygen in Combustion

The chemical revolution took place during the years 1772–78. By the later date Lavoisier had made clear to the scientific world the role of oxygen in combustion. His classic experiment, often described in elementary textbooks, was as follows: Mercury heated in common air produces a red material (an oxide we would say, a "calx" to the chemists of the eighteenth century). In a closed space about one fifth of the air disappears. The red material weighs more than the metal from which it was formed. Therefore, something has disappeared from the air and combined with the metal. The red material, the oxide or calx, is next strongly heated in an enclosed space with the sun's rays brought to a focus by a large lens or "burning glass," a gas is evolved and the metal regenerated. The new gas is the "something" which disappeared from the original air, for the amount is the same, and the calx has lost weight in the right amount. The new gas (oxygen) mixed with the residue from the first experiment yields a mixture which is identical with common air.

The experiments are simple, the proof appears to be complete. (Lavoisier, of course, generalized far beyond the case of mercury.) But the new conceptual scheme was by no means accepted at once with great acclaim. Quite the contrary. Lavoisier had to drive home his points with telling arguments. Slowly his French contemporaries were won over, but Priestley and Watt of the steam-engine fame and Cavendish and scores of others continued to cling to the phlogiston theory for a decade. Priestley's case is particularly interesting. This English experimenter had actually provided Lavoisier with an important clue when in 1774 he told him about his preparation of oxygen gas by heating red oxide of mercury. But Priestley died in 1804 without ever being converted to the new doctrine.

Why was there this reluctance to modify ideas in the light of beautifully clear experiments, and why were the men of the eighteenth century so long in getting on the right track? There were two reasons: first, one conceptual scheme —the phlogiston theory—had acquired an almost paralyzing hold on their minds; and second, elucidating the facts necessary to overthrow the theory involved experiments with gases which were then extremely difficult.

The Significance of the Phlogiston Theory

The phlogiston theory in its day was, we must first realize, a long step forward. In the sixteenth and seventeenth centuries those who were interested in making some sense out of what we now call chemistry were wandering in a bewildering forest. From the alchemists and the practical men, particularly the metal makers, they had acquired a mass of apparently unrelated facts and strange ideas about "ele-

ments." The earth, air, fire, and water concept of Aristotle
was still hovering over them. Boyle in his *Skeptical Chymist*
did a little, but not much, to clear a space in the tangled
underbrush of fact and fancy so closely interwoven and
cemented by strange words. Let us look at some of the common phenomena that had to be explained by Newton and
his contemporaries, that is to say, fitted into a conceptual
scheme. Metals could be obtained by heating certain materials with charcoal (the ancient art of winning metals
from their ores). Metals were at first sight very much the
same; they had similar superficial properties. Even today
the classification of metal and nonmetal appeals at once to
a layman. Other solids were called "earths" (oxides for us
today) or else, like charcoal or sulfur, they were "com-
bustible principles." Some earths when heated with charcoal
yielded metals. This process could be reversed, for often
but not always the metal (for example, tin) on heating
yielded an earthlike substance. From such an artificial earthlike substance (an oxide in modern terms) the metal could
be regained if the earth was heated with charcoal. A pure
earth of this sort might be called a calx, the process of forming it by heating a metal was "calcination."

How were all these facts, inherited from the Middle
Ages and before, to be fitted together? By the introduction
of a principle called phlogiston, closely related to Aristotle's old element, fire—closely related, yet the relationship was never clear. To those who sought for clarity it
seemed evident that there must be some common principle
involved in the process of making various metals from their
calces and vice versa. Therefore, let us call this something
phlogiston, they in effect declared. When phlogiston was
added to a calx you had a metal, when you removed it
from a metal a calx was formed; phlogiston was in a sense
a metalizing principle. Note there is a common-sense assumption more or less implied in this line of reasoning: except for gold, and occasionally a few other metals, calces
not metals occur in nature. Therefore, these calces were the
simpler materials, something must be added to them to make
them metals. Since metals were so alike, the "something" was

obviously the same in all cases. We shall call it phlogiston, said Becher and his pupil Stahl in a series of books published in 1703–31.

Here was a key to unlock a maze, and it was immediately accepted. Here was a concept which provided a pattern into which a mass of otherwise unrelated phenomena could be fitted. Substances were rich or poor in phlogiston, this seemed easy to establish. What was phlogiston itself? It probably was never to be seen. Substances rich in phlogiston easily took fire and, indeed, fire was perhaps a manifestation of phlogiston, or worked with it at least. For some, fire was still an element. Charcoal was a phlogiston-rich material and on heating with a metallic calx gave up its phlogiston to the calx, making a metal. By itself charcoal burned, the phlogiston appearing as fire or combined with the air. Sulfur, using the word in its modern sense, was found free in nature; it burned when heated and yielded an acid, vitriolic acid (sulfuric acid in modern terms). Clearly, this sulfur was only vitriolic acid highly "phlogisticated"; the burning set the phlogiston free and yielded the acid.

We can write these changes in diagrammatic form to illustrate how the chemists of the eighteenth century thought:

Calx + phlogiston (from charcoal) ———→ metal.
Metal heated in air———→ calx + phlogiston (to the air).
Charcoal burned yields phlogiston to the air accompanied by fire.
Phlogisticated vitriolic acid (sulfur to us) burns yielding phlogiston (to the air) + vitriolic acid (sulfuric acid).

There was one very simple flaw in all this argument and the interesting fact is that this flaw was known and talked about for fifty years before the phlogiston theory was even shaken, much less overthrown. This is a beautiful illustration of the principle in the Tactics and Strategy of Science referred to at the beginning of this section, namely, that a scientific discovery must fit the times. As early as 1630 (note the date—before Boyle was born) a Frenchman, Jean Rey, studied the calcination of tin and showed that the calx weighed more than the tin from which it was formed. More than that, he gave an explanation closely in accord with Lavoisier's ideas of 150 years later. For he said, "this increase in weight comes from the air, which in the vessel has been rendered denser, heavier, and in some measure adhesive . . . which air mixes with the calx . . . and becomes attached to its most minute particles. . . ." Boyle confirmed the increase in weight of metals in calcination in 1673 but added no support to Rey's shrewd guess (it was little more) as to the reason. In fact, if anything, he led subsequent investigators down the wrong path. At least in retrospect it seems that if he had followed up only a little more boldly his own experiments, the phlogiston theory might never have been proposed or, if proposed, never accepted seriously. Yet it is all too easy to imagine that even a still greater genius than Boyle could have discovered oxygen and revealed its role in combustion and calcination in the seventeenth century. Too much physics as well as chemistry lay under wraps which were only slowly removed by the labors of many men.

At all events, Boyle put forward the hypothesis that fire, the Aristotelian principle, had passed through the walls of the glass vessel used and combined with the metal, thereby giving it weight. This was, of course, not the same as the phlogiston theory formulated a generation later; in a sense it was the opposite because according to Boyle something was *added* to the metal in calcination, namely, fire. While in the phlogiston theory something, namely, phlogiston, was *removed*. But Boyle's writings did focus attention on the heat and flame (a characteristic of fire and calcination) rather than on the air which had figured in Rey's explanation.

A Scientific Discovery Must Fit the Times

Rey's ideas about the air seem to have been lost in the subsequent 150 years, but not the facts of calcination. That

a calx weighed more than the metal was well known throughout the eighteenth century, but this fact was *not* recognized
as being fatal to the phlogiston theory. Here is an important
point. Does it argue for the stupidity of the experimental
philosophers of the day as a few writers once would have
us think? Not at all; it merely demonstrates that in complex
affairs of science, one is concerned with trying to account
for a variety of facts and with welding them into a conceptual scheme; one fact is not by itself sufficient to wreck
the scheme. A conceptual scheme is never discarded merely
because of a few stubborn facts with which it cannot be
reconciled; a concept is either modified or replaced by a
better concept, never abandoned with nothing left to take
its place.

Not only was it known in 1770 that a calx weighed more
than the metal from which it was formed (which means to
us that something must have been taken up in its formation),
but Boyle himself back in the 1660's showed that air was
necessary for fire. John Mayow and Robert Hooke at about
the same date had written about burning and the respiration
of animals in terms of air being "deprived of its elastic
force by the breathing of animals very much in the same
way as by the burning of flame." Stephen Hales, fifty years
later, spoke the same language. But these men were all
ahead of their times. As we reread their papers we see in
spite of strange words and ill-defined ideas they had demonstrated that air in which material had been burned or
animals had respired would no longer sustain fire or life;
furthermore, they showed that there was an actual dimi-
nution of the volume of the air in such cases. All of which
seems to force the right explanation to our eyes; not so to
the chemists of the eighteenth century.

Air which would no longer support combustion had
merely become so rich in phlogiston it could take up no
more, the "phlogistonists" declared. Indeed, when Priestley
discovered how to prepare essentially pure nitrogen, it
was quite natural for him to regard it as completely "phlogisticated air," because nitrogen will not support combustion.
Likewise, when he discovered how to prepare essentially

pure oxygen gas by heating red oxide of mercury, he called it "dephlogisticated air." He found this gas to be like common air, though a candle burned in it more brightly than even in common air. Upon the whole, said Priestley, it may safely be concluded, "that the purest air is that which contains the least phlogiston: that air is impure (by which I mean that it is unfit for respiration, and for the purpose of supporting flame) in proportion as it contains more of that principle." This letter was read to the Royal Society on May 25, 1775. And in the same year in another letter he spoke of his newly discovered oxygen as "[an air] that is five or six times better than common air, for the purposes of respiration, inflammation and, I believe, every other use of common atmospherical air. As I think I have sufficiently proved that the fitness of air for respiration depends on its capacity to receive the *phlogiston* exhaled from the lungs this species of air may not improperly be called, *dephlogisticated air.*"

Experimental Difficulties with Gases

A chemist reading the papers of the phlogistonists clutches his head in despair; he seems to be transported to an Alice-through-the-looking-glass world! But if he is patient and interested he soon recognizes that much of the difficulty stemmed from the experimenters' inability to handle and characterize different gases. This fact illustrates once again the difficulty of experimentation. Metals and calxes, inflammable substances like sulfur, charcoal, and phosphorus, the chemists of the eighteenth century could recognize and manipulate since they were solids. Even some liquids like vitriolic acid, water, and mercury were quite definite individuals. But two gases, neither of which would support fire, like nitrogen and carbon dioxide, were often hopelessly confused; or two which burned, like hydrogen and carbon monoxide. Nearly all gases look alike except for the few which are colored. They are compressible and subject to thermal expansion to about the same degree. Their densities, i.e., the weight of a unit volume, differ but that was something not easy to determine in those days. Indeed, in the eighteenth century the distinction between weight and density (i.e., weight per unit volume) even for solids and liquids was often confused. The chemical properties of each gas are characteristic and the way each gas is prepared is different; and it was these differences that finally led to a straightening out of some of the tangled skein.

To understand the difficulties of the chemists of 175 years ago, imagine yourself an elementary student in a laboratory given glass bottles of air, of oxygen, of nitrogen, and one containing air saturated with ether vapor, and asked to tell whether or not all the "airs" or gases in the bottles are identical. The air containing the ether vapor (actually still largely air) will be the only one at first recognized as distinct. A student does not know how to proceed to examine these gases except by looking at them, smelling them, or testing their solubility in water. And from Boyle's day to Priestley's the experimenters were largely in the same predicament. They spoke of different "airs," but hardly knew whether the differences were real or due to the presence of some impurity. Thus, Priestley, writing in 1777, said:

"Van Helmont and other chymists who succeeded him, were acquainted with the property of some *vapours* to suffocate, and extinguish flame, and of others to be ignited. . . . But they had no idea that the substances (if, indeed they knew that they were *substances*, and not merely *properties*, and *affections* of bodies which produced those effects) were capable of being separately exhibited in the form of a *permanently elastic vapour* . . . any more than the thing that constitutes *smell*. In fact they knew nothing at all of any air besides *common air*, and therefore they applied the term to no other substances whatever. . . ."

The history of the study of gases covers a hundred years from Boyle's day. A number of important improvements in techniques were made. They were brought to a focus by Priestley who in 1772 carried out extensive and very original experiments with "airs." He improved still further several techniques of handling these airs or gases which enormously simplified the experimental procedures. Before Priestley's work only three "different airs" were known. In a few years he had discovered eleven more, including oxygen. Here is another illustration of the importance of techniques, though here we meet with an evolutionary rather than a revolutionary change.

Though Priestley was the chief figure in extending the knowledge of gases, his stubborn refusal to accept the consequences of his own discoveries has already been mentioned. It is not necessary in this chapter to discuss either Priestley or Lavoisier as individuals, though the instructor using the case history of combustion would certainly wish to do so. Nor do I propose to digress by examining the priority problems involved in the work of these two men and the Swedish chemist, Scheele, who also discovered oxygen. Such matters fall within the province of the historian of science. For the purposes of the present exposition the important questions are: Why did it take the scientists of the eighteenth century so long to get on the right road? And why were there so many stubborn travelers on the wrong road after the right one had been discovered?

The Phlogiston Theory, a Block to a New Concept

It is sometimes said that the experimenters before Lavoisier's day did not carry out quantitative experiments, that is, they did not use the balance. If they had, we are told, they would have discovered that combustion involves an increase in weight and would have rejected the phlogiston theory. This is nonsense. Rey, as I have already explained, long before the beginning of the phlogiston period showed that a calx weighed more than a metal. Quantitative experiments, though, of course, not very accurate ones, were repeatedly made. Everyone knew that a calx weighed more than the metal from which it was formed. No straightforward statement of the phlogiston theory could accommodate this fact. Yet the phlogiston theory was so useful that few if any in the mid-eighteenth century were looking to overthrow it or disprove it. Rather, they were interested in reconciling one inconvenient set of facts with what seemed from their point of view an otherwise admirable conceptual scheme. How they twisted and squirmed to accommodate the quantitative facts of calcination with the phlogiston theory makes an interesting chapter in the history of science. The eighteenth-century accounts are often confusing. Fortunately their many details need not concern the readers of this book; nor except in broad outline need they concern one teaching the principles of the Tactics and Strategy of Science with the aid of the eighteenth-century studies on combustion.

The principle which emerges is one already encountered, namely, that it takes a new conceptual scheme to cause the abandonment of an old one: when only a few facts appear to be irreconcilable with a well-established conceptual scheme, the first attempt is *not* to discard the scheme but to find some way out of the difficulty and keep it. Likewise the proponents of new concepts are rarely shaken by a few alleged facts to the contrary. They seek at first to prove them wrong or to circumvent them. Thus Lavoisier persisted with his own new concept in spite of the fact that certain experiments seemed to be completely inexplicable in its terms. It was later found that the interpretation of the experiments was in error. Not so in the case of the calcination of metals: there could be no doubt in the mind of anyone by 1770 that the increase in weight during calcination was real. There was also no doubt that there should be a loss in weight according to the phlogiston theory. Or at best no change in weight if phlogiston were an imponderable substance like fire.

Attempts to Reconstruct the Phlogiston Theory

One attempt to get out of the dilemma of calcination took refuge in a confusion between weight and density (calxes are less dense than metals, but the total weight in the calcination increased). This was soon put right by clear thinking. Another attempt involved assigning a negative weight to phlogiston. This illustrates how desperately men may strive to modify an old idea to make it accord with new experi-

ments. But in this case the modification represented not a
step forward but several steps to the rear! What was gained
by accommodating the quantitative aspect of calcination
was lost by following the consequences of negative weight
to a logical conclusion. What manner of substance or principle could phlogiston be that when it was added to another
material the total mass or weight diminished? The idea that
phlogiston had negative weight strained the credulity, and
for the most part this logical extension of the phlogiston
theory (logical in one sense, highly illogical in another) was
never widely accepted. But before we laugh too hard at
the investigators of the eighteenth century, let us remember
that before the nineteenth century heat was considered a
corporeal substance and the whole concept of the atomic
and molecular theory of matter lay over the distant horizon.

To some of the chemical experimenters, the dilemma
presented by the quantitative facts of calcination seems to
have been accepted as just one of those things which cannot be fitted in. And this attitude is much more common in
the history of science than most historians would have you
believe. Indeed, it is in a way a necessary attitude at certain stages of development of any concept. The keen-
minded scientist, the real genius, is the man who keeps in
the forefront of his thoughts these unsolved riddles. He
then is ready to relate a new discovery or a new technique
to the unsolved problems. He is the pioneer, the revolu-
tionist. And it is this combination of strategy and tactics
in the hands of a master which is well worthy of study if
one would try to understand science through the historical
approach.

Lavoisier's Clue

To recount the history of Lavoisier's development of his new
theory, and the way in which the new discoveries of the
time were fitted into his scheme would mean the recital of
a long story. Such an account would be out of place in this
volume, though a considerable portion of it would be involved in a thorough study of the case histories at hand.

Let me take a few moments of the reader's time, however, to point out how Lavoisier first seems to have taken the right turn in the road. In a famous note of 1772, he wrote as follows:

"About eight days ago I discovered that sulphur in burning, far from losing weight, on the contrary gains it; . . . it is the same with phosphorus; this increase of weight arises from a prodigious quantity of air that is fixed during the combustion and combines with the vapours.

"This discovery, which I have established by experiments that I regard as decisive, has led me to think that what is observed in the combustion of sulphur and phosphorus may well take place in the case of all substances that gain in weight by combustion and calcination: and I am persuaded that the increase in weight of metallic calces is due to the same cause. . . ."

Here we seem to see the mental process at work to which I referred a few moments ago; the perception that a new fact properly interpreted enables one to explain an old dilemma, an outstanding unsolved problem. In a sense, in this note Lavoisier outlined the whole new chemistry, as he always later claimed. (The note was deposited sealed with the Secretary of the French Academy on November 1, 1772.) To be sure, at first Lavoisier mistook the gas evolved in the reduction of a calx with charcoal (carbon dioxide, the "fixed air" of that day) with the gas absorbed in calcination. The study we can now make of his notebooks as well as his later publications makes it plain that it was not until after Priestley's discovery of oxygen and Lavoisier's repetition of some of Priestley's experiments with the new gas that the nature of the gas absorbed in calcination became clear. It was only then that all the pieces of the puzzle fitted together, with the newly discovered oxygen occupying the central position in the picture. But at the outset Lavoisier recognized that something was absorbed from the air. Unconsciously he was retracing the steps Jean Rey had taken nearly 150 years earlier and which had never been followed up. Rey's almost forgotten book was called to Lavoisier's attention shortly after his first publications of his new theory.

An interesting question that will at once come to the mind of many is the following: why did the study of sulfur and phosphorus lead Lavoisier to the right type of explanation? Why after experiments with those substances did he set out full of confidence on a set of planned experiments along a new line? This is one of those historical riddles which can never be answered, but concerning which it is not entirely profitless to speculate. I suggest that the key word in Lavoisier's note of November 1, 1772, is "prodigious"—"this increase of weight arises from a prodigious quantity of air that is fixed." If this is so, we have again another illustration of how experimental difficulties or the lack of them condition the evolution of new concepts. To determine whether air is absorbed or not during the calcination of a metal is not easy; the process takes a long time, a high temperature, and both the increase in weight and the amount of oxygen absorbed are small. But with phosphorus and sulfur the experiment was relatively easy to perform (the materials burn at once on ignition with a burning glass); furthermore, the effect observed is very large. The reason for this in terms of modern chemistry is that sulfur and phosphorus have low atomic weights of 32 and 31 (oxygen is 16), and in the combustion 1 atom of phosphorus combines with 5 of oxygen; 1 atom of sulfur with 3 of oxygen. The atomic weight of the metals is high, the number of atoms of oxygen combining with them, fewer. Thus 62 weights of phosphorus will yield $62 + (5 \times 16) = 142$ parts of combustion product; while in the case of tin, the atomic weight is 118 and only 2 atoms of oxygen are involved. Thus 118 weights of tin would yield only $118 + (2 \times 16) = 150$ weights of calx or an increase of only about 25 per cent. Note that with phosphorus the increase is more than double. The corresponding differences would be reflected in the volume of oxygen absorbed, and furthermore, since the calcination of tin was a long process at a high temperature in a furnace, no entirely satisfactory way of measuring the volume of air absorbed was at hand in 1770.

Quantitative Measurements and Accidental Errors

As a matter of fact, until Lavoisier was put on the track of the gas prepared by heating mercuric oxide by Priestley, he had a hard time proving that metallic calxes did gain in weight *because* of absorption of something from the air. The method he used was to repeat certain experiments of Boyle with a slight modification. Both the modification and the difficulties are of interest and point an obvious moral to the tale. Boyle had sealed tin in a glass vessel and heated the vessel a long time on a charcoal fire (which he says is a very dangerous operation as the glass may well explode). Boyle then removed the vessel from the fire and after cooling opened the glass, reweighed the vessel and noted the increase in weight. This was one of the many well-known experiments showing that the calx weighed more than the metal. (Boyle, the reader will recall, believed the increase to be due to the fire particles which passed through the glass). Now, said Lavoisier, where Boyle went wrong was in not weighing the vessel *before* opening it. For if his explanation were right and the fire had passed through the glass and combined with the tin, the increase would have occurred before the air was admitted. While if oxygen were involved, the increase in weight would occur *after* the air was admitted. The results obtained by Lavoisier on repeating this experiment were as expected, but were far from being as striking as those obtained with phosphorus for the reasons just explained. The increase was 10 parts in a total of 4,100 in one experiment and 3 parts in about the same amount in another! We now know that the difficulties of weighing a large glass vessel with a high degree of accuracy are great, due to film moisture and electrical charges. It is, therefore, not surprising that the glass retort, after heating, varied in weight from day to day almost as much as the total gain in weight in one of the two experiments.

These tough facts of experimentation are of great importance. To me, they indicate strongly that even if Boyle had weighed his vessel before and after admitting the air, the uncertainties of his figures would probably have been so great as to confuse him and subsequent investigators. *Important advances in science are based on quantitative measurements only if the measured quantity is large as compared with possible systematic and accidental errors.* The principle of significant figures which plays so large a part in later scientific history is foreshadowed in a crude way by this episode involving the combustion of phosphorus and the calcination of tin. Therefore, in considering the case history at hand the instructor would undoubtedly wish to enlarge at some length on the whole problem of the controlled variable and the role of quantitative measurements.

Lavoisier and Priestley's Stubborn Facts

For students who had some prior knowledge of chemistry, say a good high-school course, the study of the last days of the phlogiston theory might be rewarding. For the controversy between Lavoisier and Priestley not only illustrates with what tenacity an able man may cling to a hopeless position, but also the boldness with which the innovator pushes forward. Even if a few facts appear to be to the contrary, he still pushes his new ideas just as his conservative opponent stoutly maintains his own tenets in spite of contradictory evidence. In such tugs of war which are the commonest experience in science, though usually in highly restricted areas and with limited significance, the innovator is by no means always right. This point needs to be made perfectly clear. Several case histories to this end would be worth recounting. A few dramatic instances would be in order where some bold man put forward a new idea based on alleged facts which turned out to be erroneous or erroneously interpreted.

The record of Lavoisier was the opposite. For the facts

he ignored were indeed not facts at all. Priestley's main points against Lavoisier's views were based on a mistaken identification of two different gases. This fact again emphasizes the difficulties of experimentation. Two gases, both inflammable, carbon monoxide and hydrogen, were at that period confused, even by the great experimenters with gases. Assuming their identity Priestley could ask Lavoisier to account for phenomena which were indeed inexplicable according to the new chemistry, but could be accommodated in the phlogiston theory, now being twisted more each day to conform to new discoveries. Not until long after Lavoisier's execution in 1794 was the relationship between the two gases straightened out. Therefore, Lavoisier was never able to respond to the most weighty of Priestley's arguments against his doctrine. He merely ignored the alleged facts, much as Priestley ignored the unexplained gain in weight or calcination. Each undoubtedly believed that some way would be found around the difficulty in question. Lavoisier's hopes, not Priestley's, proved well founded. So proceeds the course of science. Sometimes it turns out that difficulties with a concept or conceptual scheme are wisely ignored, sometimes unwisely. To suppose, with some who write about the "scientific method," that a scientific theory stands or falls on the issue of one experiment is to misunderstand science indeed.

A study of the overthrow of the phlogiston theory is thus seen to be more than a single case history; it is a related series of case histories. The student's knowledge of chemistry or willingness to take time to obtain this knowledge would be the limiting factor on the use of this material. Even without prior study of chemistry, I believe, a profitable excursion into this complicated bit of scientific history could be undertaken. From such an excursion would come a deeper appreciation of the two principles to which I earlier referred in this chapter. Having studied the phlogiston theory no one would fail to realize that old concepts may present barriers to the development of new ones; having traced the course of the history of experiments with gases and calcination, no one could fail to realize that scientific discoveries must fit the times if they are to be fruitful. In addition, other principles of the Tactics and Strategy of Science are constantly recurring throughout the somewhat lengthy story: the influence of new techniques, the difficulties of experimentation, the value of the controlled experiment, the evaluation of new concepts from experiment—all these are to be found illustrated more than once by those who have patience to study a strange and often neglected chapter in the history of science.

The works of two great biologists offer an interesting contrast in scientific method. As he toured the Galapagos, Darwin observed minor variations in the species inhabiting neighboring islands and had the genius to wonder whether they were due to factors other than separate creation. He made no experiments—there were none he could make. Decades later, an Austrian monk, Gregor Mendel, also wondered about minor variations, in particular the colors of garden peas. His problem, unlike Darwin's, lent itself to direct testing. He was able to control the breeding of his plants, and his garden thus became a laboratory. Experiment resulted in hypothesis which further experiment substantiated.

A similar contrast may be drawn between the methods described by Douglas Johnson and Claude Bernard. Johnson's research is basically observational. Bernard, on the other hand, is a master of the controlled experiment. If he wishes, he can make sure that his conditions are identical and that, therefore, science being what it is, his results will also be identical. Or he can vary the conditions, and thus test the truth or falsity of his hypotheses.

In the medical sciences, Bernard's position as an experimental genius is unexcelled. His reputation among laymen is perhaps dwarfed by the more spectacular discoveries of his fellow countryman and contemporary Pasteur; but in fecundity of ideas, in technical proficiency, and in the greatness of their discoveries, they are of equal rank. Bernard was born at Saint-Julien in 1813 and died at Paris in 1878. As a young man he journeyed to the metropolis with an unacted tragedy under his arm, determined to become a playwright. The critic Girardin suggested that he learn a profession in order to keep alive, and Bernard, following this advice, became an interne at the Hôtel-Dieu. In his subsequent career he made four contributions of the first rank to physiology: the discovery of the vasomotor nerves, the description of the action of curare and other poisons on neuromuscular activity, the production of glycogen by the liver, and the function of pancreatic juice in digestion. His conclusion that "the primary condition for freedom and independence of existence . . . is the mechanism . . . which insures in the milieu intérieur the maintenance of all the conditions necessary to the life of the elements" is one of the fundamental tenets of physiology. A plain man, Bernard lived simply despite the honors that were showered on him. His death was nationally mourned—he was the first scientist whom France honored with a public funeral.

An Introduction to the Study of Experimental Medicine, from which this selection is taken, is recognized as a classic work.

EXAMPLES OF EXPERIMENTAL PHYSIOLOGICAL INVESTIGATION

CLAUDE BERNARD

IN SCIENTIFIC INVESTIGATIONS, various circumstances may serve as starting points for research; I will reduce all these varieties, however, to two chief types:
1] Where the starting point for experimental research is an observation;
2] Where the starting point for experimental research is an hypothesis or a theory.

1. *Where the Starting Point for Experimental Research Is an Observation*

Experimental ideas are often born by chance, with the help of some casual observation. Nothing is more common; and this is really the simplest way of beginning a piece of scientific work. We take a walk, so to speak, in the realm of science, and we pursue what happens to present itself to our eyes. Bacon compares scientific investigation with hunting; the observations that present themselves are the game. Keeping the same simile, we may add that, if the game presents itself when we are looking for it, it may also present itself when we are not looking for it, or when we are looking for game of another kind. I shall cite an example in which these two cases presented themselves in succession. At the same time I shall be careful to analyze every circumstance involved.

FIRST EXAMPLE. One day, rabbits from the market were brought into my laboratory. They were put on the table where they urinated, and I happened to observe that their urine was clear and acid. This fact struck me, because rabbits, which are herbivora, generally have turbid and alkaline urine; while on the other hand carnivora, as we know, have clear and acid urine. This observation of acidity in the rabbits' urine gave me an idea that these animals must be in the nutritional condition of carnivora. I assumed that they had probably not eaten for a long time, and that they had been transformed by fasting, into veritable carnivorous animals, living on their own blood. Nothing was easier than to verify this preconceived idea or hypothesis by experiment. I gave the rabbits grass to eat; and a few hours later, their urine became turbid and alkaline. I then subjected them to fasting and after twenty-four hours or thirty-six hours at most, their urine again became clear and strongly acid; then after eating grass, their urine became alkaline again, etc. I repeated this very simple experiment a great many times, and always with the same result. I then repeated it on a horse, an herbivorous animal which also has turbid and alkaline urine. I found that fasting, as in rabbits, produced prompt acidity of the urine, with such an increase in urea, that it spontaneously crystallizes at times in the cooled urine. As a result of my experiments, I thus reached the general proposition which then was still unknown, to wit, that all fasting animals feed on meat, so that herbivora then have urine like that of carnivora.

We are here dealing with a very simple, particular fact which allows us easily to follow the evolution of experimental reasoning. When we see a phenomenon which we are not in the habit of seeing, we must always ask ourselves what it is connected with, or putting it differently, what is its proximate cause; the answer or the idea, which presents itself to the mind, must then be submitted to experiment. When I saw the rabbits' acid urine, I instinctively asked myself what could be its cause. The experimental idea consisted in the connection, which my mind spontaneously made, between acidity of the rabbits' urine, and the state of fasting which I considered equivalent to a true flesh-eater's diet. The inductive reasoning which I implicitly went through was the following syllogism: the urine of carnivora is acid; now the rabbits before me have acid urine, therefore they are carnivora, i.e., fasting. This remained to be established by experiment.

But to prove that my fasting rabbits were really carnivorous, a counterproof was required. A carnivorous rabbit had to be experimentally produced by feeding it with meat, so as to see if its urine would then be clear, as it was during fasting. So I had rabbits fed on cold boiled beef (which they eat very nicely when they are given nothing else). My expectation was again verified, and, as long as the animal diet was continued, the rabbits kept their clear and acid urine.

To complete my experiment, I made an autopsy on my animals, to see if meat was digested in the same way in rabbits as in carnivora. I found, in fact, all the phenomena of an excellent digestion in their intestinal reactions, and I noted that all the chyliferous vessels were gorged with very abundant white, milky chyle, just as in carnivora. But *à propos* of these autopsies which confirmed my ideas on meat digestion in rabbits, lo and behold a fact presented itself which I had not remotely thought of, but which became, as we shall see, my starting point in a new piece of work.

SECOND EXAMPLE (Sequel to the last). In sacrificing the rabbits which I had fed on the meat, I happened to notice that the white and milky lymphatics were first visible in the small intestine at the lower part of the duodenum, about thirty centimeters below the pylorus. This fact caught my attention because in dogs they are first visible much higher in the duodenum just below the pylorus. On examining more closely, I noted that this peculiarity in rabbits coincided with the position of the pancreatic duct which was inserted very low and near the exact place where the lymphatics began to contain a chyle made white and milky by emulsion of fatty nutritive materials.

Chance observation of this fact evoked the idea which brought to birth the thought in my mind, that pancreatic juice might well cause the emulsion of fatty materials and consequently their absorption by the lymphatic vessels. Instinctively again, I made the following syllogism: the white chyle is due to emulsion of the fat; now in rabbits white chyle is formed at the level where pancreatic juice is poured into the intestine; therefore it is pancreatic juice that makes the emulsion of fat and forms the white chyle. This had to be decided by experiment.

In view of this preconceived idea I imagined and at once performed a suitable experiment to verify the truth or falsity of my suppositions. The experiment consisted in trying the properties of pancreatic juice directly on neutral fats. But pancreatic juice does not spontaneously flow outside of the body, like saliva, for instance, or urine; its secretory organ is, on the contrary, lodged deep in the abdominal cavity. I was therefore forced to use the method of experimentation to secure the pancreatic fluid from living animals in suitable physiological conditions and in sufficient quantity. Only then could I carry out my experiment, that is to say, control my preconceived idea; and the experiment proved that my idea was correct. In fact pancreatic juice obtained in suitable conditions from dogs, rabbits and various other animals, and mixed with oil or melted fat, always instantly emulsified, and later split these fatty bodies into fatty acids, glycerine, etc., etc., by means of a specific ferment.

I shall not follow these experiments further, having explained them at length in a special work. I wish here to show merely how an accidental first observation of the acidity of rabbits' urine suggested to me the idea of making experiments on them with carnivorous feeding, and how later, in continuing these experiments, I brought to light, without seeing it, another observation concerning the peculiar arrangement of the junction of the pancreatic duct in rabbits. This second observation gave me, in turn, the idea of experimenting on the behavior of pancreatic juice.

From the above examples we see how chance observation of a fact or phenomenon brings to birth, by anticipation, a preconceived idea or hypothesis about the probable cause of the phenomenon observed; how the preconceived idea begets reasoning which results in the experiment which verifies it; how, in one case, we had to have recourse to experimentation, i.e., to the use of more or less complicated operative processes, etc., to work out the verification. In the last example, experiment played a double rôle; it first judged and confirmed the provisions of the reasoning which it had begotten; but what is more, it produced a fresh observation. We may therefore call this observation an observation produced or begotten by experiment. This proves that, as we said, all the results of an experiment must be observed, both those connected with the preconceived idea and those without any relation to it. If we saw only facts connected with our preconceived idea, we should often cut ourselves off from making discoveries. For it often happens that an unsuccessful experiment may produce an excellent observation, as the following example will prove.

THIRD EXAMPLE.   In 1857, I undertook a series of experiments on the elimination of substances in the urine, and this time the results of the experiment, unlike the previous examples, did not confirm my previsions or preconceived ideas. I had therefore made what we habitually call an unsuccessful experiment. But there are no unsuccessful experiments; for, when they do not serve the investigation for which they were devised, we must still profit by observation to find occasion for other experiments.

In investigating how the blood, leaving the kidney, eliminated substances that I had injected, I chanced to observe that the blood in the renal vein was crimson, while the blood in the neighboring veins was dark like ordinary venous blood. This unexpected peculiarity struck me, and I thus made observation of a fresh fact begotten by the experiment, but foreign to the experimental aim pursued at the moment. I therefore gave up my unverified original idea, and directed my attention to the singular coloring of the venous renal blood; and when I had noted it well and assured myself that there was no source of error in my observation, I naturally asked myself what could be its cause. As I examined the urine flowing through the urethra and reflected about it, it occurred to me that the red coloring of the venous blood might well be connected with the secreting or active state of the kidney. On this hypothesis, if the renal secretion was stopped, the venous blood should become dark: that is what happened; when the renal secretion was re-established, the venous blood should become crimson again; this I also succeeded in verifying whenever I excited the secretion of urine. I thus secured experimental proof that there is a connection between the secretion of urine and the coloring of blood in the renal vein.

But that is still by no means all. In the normal state, venous blood in the kidney is almost constantly crimson, because the urinary organ secretes almost continuously, though alternately for each kidney. Now I wished to know whether the crimson color is a general fact characteristic of the other glands, and in this way to get a clear-cut counterproof demonstrating that the phenomenon of secretion itself was what led to the alteration in the color of the venous blood. I reasoned thus: if, said I, secretion, as it seems to be, causes the crimson color of glandular venous blood, then, in such glandular organs as the salivary glands which secrete intermittently, the venous blood will change color intermittently and become dark, while the gland is at rest, and red during secretion. So I uncovered a dog's submaxillary gland, its ducts, its nerves and its vessels. In its normal state, this gland supplies an intermittent secretion which we can excite or stop at pleasure. Now while the gland was at rest, and nothing flowed through the salivary duct, I clearly noted that the venous blood was, indeed dark, while, as soon as secretion appeared, the blood became crimson, to resume its dark color when the secretion stopped; and it remained dark as long as the intermission lasted, etc.

These last observations later became the starting point for new ideas which guided me in making investigations as to the chemical cause of the change in color of glandular blood during secretion. I shall not further describe these experiments which, moreover, I have published in detail. It is enough for me to prove that scientific investigations and experimental ideas may have their birth in almost involuntary chance observations which present themselves either spontaneously or in an experiment made with a different purpose.

Let me cite another case,—one in which an experimenter produces an observation and voluntarily brings it to birth. This case is, so to speak, included in the preceding case; but it differs from it in this, that, instead of waiting for an observation to present itself by chance in fortuitous circumstances, we produce it by experiment. Returning to Bacon's comparison, we might say that an experimenter, in this instance, is like a hunter who, instead of waiting quietly for game, tries to make it rise, by beating up the locality where he assumes it is. We use this method whenever we have no preconceived idea in respect to a subject as to which previous observations are lacking. So we experiment to bring to birth observations which in turn may bring to birth ideas. This continually occurs in medicine when we wish to investigate the action of a poison or of some medicinal substance, or an animal's economy; we make experiments to see, and we then take our direction from what we have seen.

FOURTH EXAMPLE. In 1845, Monsieur Pelouze gave me a toxic substance, called *curare*, which had been brought to him from America. We then knew nothing about the physiological action of this substance. From old observations and from the interesting accounts of Alex. von Humboldt and of Roulin and Boussingault, we knew only that the preparation of this substance was complex and difficult, and that it very speedily kills an animal if introduced under the skin. But from the earlier observations, I could get no idea of the mechanism of death by curare; to get such an idea I had to make fresh observations as to the organic disturbances to which this poison might lead. I therefore made experiments *to see* things about which I had absolutely no preconceived idea. First, I put curare under the skin of a frog: it died after a few minutes; I opened it at once, and in this physiological autopsy I studied in succession what had become of the known physiological properties of its various tissues. I say physiological autopsy purposely, because no others are really instructive. The disappearance of physiological properties is what explains death, and not anatomical changes. Indeed, in the present state of science, we see physiological properties disappear in any number of cases without being able to show, by our present means of observation, any corresponding anatomical change; such, for example, is the case with curare. Meantime, we shall find examples, on the contrary, in which physiological properties persist, in spite of very marked anatomical changes with which the functions are by no means incompatible. Now in my frog poisoned with curare, the heart maintained its movements, the blood was apparently no more changed in physiological properties than the muscles, which kept their normal contractility. But while the nervous system had kept its normal anatomical appearance, the properties of the nerves had nevertheless completely disappeared. There were

no movements, either voluntary or reflex, and when the
motor nerves were stimulated directly, they no longer
caused any contraction in the muscles. To learn whether
there was anything accidental or mistaken in this first
observation, I repeated it several times and verified it in
various ways; for when we wish to reason experimentally,
the first thing necessary is to be a good observer and to
make quite certain that the starting point of our reasoning
is not a mistake in observation. In mammals and in birds,
I found the same phenomena as in frogs, and disappearance
of the physiological properties of the motor nervous system
became my constant fact. Starting from this well-established
fact, I could then carry analysis of the phenomena further
and determine the mechanism of death from curare. I still
proceeded by reasonings analogous to those quoted in the
above example, and, from idea to idea and experiment to
experiment, I progressed to more and more definite facts.
I finally reached this general proposition, that *curare causes
death by destroying all the motor nerves, without affecting
the sensory nerves.*

In cases where we make an experiment in which both
preconceived idea and reasoning seem completely lacking,
we yet necessarily reason by syllogism without knowing it.
In the case of curare, I instinctively reasoned in the following
way: no phenomenon is without a cause, and consequently
no poisoning without a physiological lesion peculiar or proper to the poison used; now, thought I, curare must cause
death by an activity special to itself and by acting on
certain definite organic parts. So by poisoning an animal
with curare and by examining the properties of its various
tissues immediately after death, I can perhaps find and
study the lesions peculiar to it.

The mind, then, is still active here, and an experiment in
order to see is included, nevertheless, in our general definition of an experiment. In every enterprise, in fact, the mind
is always reasoning, and, even when we seem to act without
a motive, an instinctive logic still directs the mind. Only we
are not aware of it, because we begin by reasoning before
we know or say that we are reasoning, just as we begin by

speaking before we observe that we are speaking, and just as we begin by seeing and hearing before we know what we see or what we hear.

FIFTH EXAMPLE.   About 1846, I wished to make experiments on the cause of poisoning with carbon monoxide. I knew that this gas had been described as toxic, but I knew literally nothing about the mechanism of its poisoning; I therefore could not have a preconceived opinion. What, then, was to be done? I must bring to birth an idea by making a fact appear, i.e., make another experiment to see. In fact I poisoned a dog by making him breathe carbon monoxide and after death I at once opened his body. I looked at the state of the organs and fluids. What caught my attention at once was that its blood was scarlet in all the vessels, in the veins as well as the arteries, in the right heart as well as in the left. I repeated the experiment on rabbits, birds and frogs, and everywhere I found the same scarlet coloring of the blood. But I was diverted from continuing this investigation, and I kept this observation a long time unused except for quoting it in my course *à propos* of the coloring of blood.

In 1856, no one had carried the experimental question further, and in my course at the Collège de France on toxic and medicinal substances, I again took up the study of poisoning by carbon monoxide which I had begun in 1846. I found myself then in a confused situation, for at this time I already knew that poisoning with carbon monoxide makes the blood scarlet in the whole circulatory system. I had to make hypotheses, and establish a preconceived idea about my first observation, so as to go ahead. Now, reflecting on the fact of scarlet blood, I tried to interpret it by my earlier knowledge as to the cause of the color of blood. Whereupon all the following reflections presented themselves to my mind. The scarlet color, said I, is peculiar to arterial blood and connected with the presence of a large proportion of oxygen, while dark coloring belongs with absence of oxygen and presence of a larger proportion of carbonic acid; so the idea occurred to me that carbon monoxide, by keeping venous blood scarlet, might perhaps have prevented the oxygen from changing into carbonic acid in the capillaries. Yet it seemed hard to understand how that could be the cause of death. But still keeping on with my inner preconceived reasoning, I added: If that is true, blood taken from the veins of animals poisoned with carbon monoxide should be like arterial blood in containing oxygen; we must see if that is the fact.

Following this reasoning, based on interpretation of my observation, I tried an experiment to verify my hypothesis as to the persistence of oxygen in the venous blood. I passed a current of hydrogen through scarlet venous blood taken from an animal poisoned with carbon monoxide, but I could not liberate the oxygen as usual. I tried to do the same with arterial blood; I had no greater success. My preconceived idea was therefore false. But the impossibility of getting oxygen from the blood of a dog poisoned with carbon monoxide was a second observation which suggested a fresh hypothesis. What could have become of the oxygen in the blood? It had not changed into carbonic acid, because I had not set free large quantities of that gas in passing a current of hydrogen through the blood of the poisoned animals. Moreover, that hypothesis was contrary to the color of the blood. I exhausted myself in conjectures about how carbon monoxide could cause the oxygen to disappear from the blood; and as gases displace one another I naturally thought that the carbon monoxide might have displaced the oxygen and driven it out of the blood. To learn this, I decided to vary my experimentation by putting the blood in artificial conditions that would allow me to recover the displaced oxygen. So I studied the action of carbon monoxide on blood experimentally. For this purpose I took a certain amount of arterial blood from a healthy animal; I put this blood on the mercury in an inverted test tube containing carbon monoxide; I then shook the whole thing so as to poison the blood sheltered from contact with the outer air. Then, after an interval, I examined whether the air in the test-tube in contact with the poisoned blood had been changed, and I noted that the air thus in contact with the blood had been remarkably enriched with oxygen, while the proportion of carbon monoxide was lessened. Repeated in the same conditions, these experiments taught me that what had occurred was an exchange, volume by volume, between the carbon monoxide and the oxygen of the blood. But the carbon monoxide, in displacing the oxygen that it had expelled from the blood, remained chemically combined in the blood and could no longer be displaced either by oxygen or by other gases. So that death came through death of the molecules of blood, or in other words by stopping their exercise of a physiological property essential to life.

This last example, which I have very briefly described, is complete; it shows from one end to the other, how we proceed with the experimental method and succeeded in learning the immediate cause of phenomena. To begin with I knew literally nothing about the mechanism of the phenomenon of poisoning with carbon monoxide. I undertook an experiment to see, i.e., to observe. I made a preliminary observation of a special change in the coloring of blood. I interpreted this observation, and I made an hypothesis which proved false. But the experiment provided me with a second observation about which I reasoned anew, using it as a starting point for making a new hypothesis as to the mechanism, by which the oxygen in the blood was removed. By building up hypotheses, one by one, about the facts as I observed them, I finally succeeded in showing that carbon monoxide replaces oxygen in a molecule of blood, by combining with the substance of the molecule. Experimental analysis, here, has reached its goal. This is one of the cases, rare in physiology, which I am happy to be able to quote. Here the immediate cause of the phenomenon of poisoning is found and is translated into a theory which accounts for all the facts and at the same time includes all the observations and experiments. Formulated as follows, the theory posits the main facts from which all the rest are deduced: Carbon monoxide combines more intimately than oxygen with the hemoglobin in a molecule of blood. It has quite recently been proved that carbon mon-oxide forms a definite combination with hemoglobin. So that the molecule of blood, as if petrified by the stability of the combination, loses its vital properties. Hence everything is logically deduced: because of its property of more intimate combination, carbon monoxide drives out of the blood the oxygen essential to life; the molecules of blood become inert, and the animal dies, with symptoms of hemorrhage, from true paralysis of the molecules.

But when a theory is sound and indeed shows the real and definite physico-chemical cause of phenomena, it not only includes the observed facts but predicts others and leads to rational applications that are logical consequences of the theory. Here again we meet this criterion. In fact, if carbon monoxide has the property of driving out oxygen by taking its place in combining with a molecule of blood, we should be able to use the gas to analyze the gases in blood, and especially for determining oxygen. From my experi-ments I deduced this application which has been generally adopted today. Applications of this property of carbon monoxide have been made in legal medicine for finding the coloring matter of blood; and from the physiological facts described above we may also already deduce results con-nected with hygiene, experimental pathology, and notably with the mechanism of certain forms of anemia.

As in every other case, all the deductions from the theory doubtless still require experimental verification; and logic does not suffice. But this is because the conditions in which carbon monoxide acts on the blood may present other com-plex circumstances and any number of details which the theory cannot yet predict. Otherwise, we could reach con-clusions by logic alone, without any need of experimental verifications. Because of possible unforeseen and variable new elements in the conditions of a phenomenon, logic alone can in experimental science never suffice. Even when we have a theory that seems sound, it is never more than rela-tively sound, and it always includes a certain proportion of the unknown.

II. When the Starting Point of Experimental Research Is an Hypothesis or a Theory

In noting an observation we must never go beyond facts. But in making an experiment, it is different. I wish to show that hypotheses are indispensable, and that they are useful, therefore, precisely because they lead us outside of facts and carry science forward. The object of hypotheses is not only to make us try new experiments; they also often make us discover new facts which we should not have perceived without them. In the preceding examples, we saw that we can start from a particular fact and rise one by one to more general ideas, i.e., to a theory. But as we have just seen, we can also sometimes start with an hypothesis deduced from a theory. Though we are dealing in this case with reasoning logically deduced from a theory, we have an hypothesis that must still be verified by experiment. Indeed, theories are only an assembling of the earlier facts, on which our hypothesis rests, and cannot be used to demonstrate it experimentally. We said that, in this instance, we must not submit to the yoke of theories, and that keeping our mental independence is the best way to discover the truth. This is proved by the following examples.

FIRST EXAMPLE. In 1843, in one of my first pieces of work, I undertook to study what becomes of different alimentary substances in nutrition. I began with sugar, a definite substance that is easier than any other to recognize and follow in the bodily economy. With this in view, I injected solutions of cane sugar into the blood of animals, and I noted that even when injected in weak doses the sugar passed into the urine. I recognized later that, by changing or transforming sugar, the gastric juice made it capable of assimilation, i.e., of destruction in the blood.

Thereupon I wished to learn in what organ the nutritive sugar disappeared, and I conceived the hypothesis that sugar introduced into the blood through nutrition might be destroyed in the lungs or in the general capillaries. The

theory, indeed, which then prevailed and which was naturally my proper starting point, assumed that the sugar present
in animals came exclusively from foods, and that it was
destroyed in animal organisms by the phenomena of combustion, i.e., of respiration. Thus sugar had gained the name
of *respiratory nutriment*. But I was immediately led to see
that the theory about the origin of sugar in animals, which
served me as a starting point, was false. As a result of the
experiments which I shall describe further on, I was not
indeed led to find an organ for destroying sugar, but, on
the contrary, I discovered an organ for making it, and I
found that all animal blood contains sugar even when they
do not eat it. So I noted a new fact, unforeseen in theory,
which men had not noticed, doubtless because they were
under the influence of contrary theories which they had too
confidently accepted. I therefore abandoned my hypothesis
on the spot, so as to pursue the unexpected result which
has since become the fertile origin of a new path for investigation and a mine of discoveries that is not yet exhausted.

In these researches I followed the principles of the experimental method that we have established, i.e., that, in
presence of a well-noted, new fact which contradicts a
theory, instead of keeping the theory and abandoning the
fact, I should keep and study the fact, and I hastened to
give up the theory, thus conforming to the precept: "When
we meet a fact which contradicts a prevailing theory, we
must accept the fact and abandon the theory, even when
the theory is supported by great names and generally accepted."

We must therefore distinguish, as we said, between
principles and theories, and never believe absolutely in the
latter. We had a theory here which assumed that the vege-
table kingdom alone had the power of creating the individual
compounds which the animal kingdom is supposed to destroy. According to this theory, established and supported
by the most illustrious chemists of our day, animals were
incapable of producing sugar in their organisms. If I had
believed in this theory absolutely, I should have had to
conclude that my experiment was vitiated by some inac-

curacy; and less wary experimenters than I might have condemned it at once, and might not have tarried longer at an observation which could be theoretically suspected of including sources of error, since it showed sugar in the blood of animals on a diet that lacked starchy or sugary materials. But instead of being concerned about the theory, I concerned myself only with the fact whose reality I was trying to establish. By new experiments and by means of suitable counterproofs, I was thus led to confirm my first observation and to find that the liver is the organ in which animal sugar is formed in certain given circumstances, to spread later into the whole blood supply and into the tissues and fluids.

Animal glycogenesis which I thus discovered, i.e., the power of producing sugar, possessed by animals as well as vegetables, is now an acquired fact for science; but we have not yet fixed on a plausible theory accounting for the phenomenon. The fresh facts which I made known are the source of numerous studies and many varied theories in apparent contradiction with each other and with my own. When entering on new ground we must not be afraid to express even risky ideas so as to stimulate research in all directions. As Priestley put it, we must not remain inactive through false modesty based on fear of being mistaken. So I made more or less hypothetical theories of glycogenesis; after mine came others; my theories, like other men's, will live the allotted life of necessarily very partial and temporary theories at the opening of a new series of investigations; they will be replaced later by others, embodying a more advanced stage of the question, and so on. Theories are like a stairway; by climbing, science widens its horizon more and more, because theories embody and necessarily include proportionately more facts as they advance. Progress is achieved by exchanging our theories for new ones which go further than the old, until we find one based on a larger number of facts. In the case which now concerns us, the question is not one of condemning the old to the advantage of a more recent theory. What is important is having opened a new road; for well-observed facts, though brought to light by passing theories, will never die; they are the material on which alone the house of science will at last be built, when it has facts enough and has gone sufficiently deep into the analysis of phenomena to know their law or their causation.

To sum up, theories are only hypotheses, verified by more or less numerous facts. Those verified by the most facts are the best; but even then they are never final, never to be absolutely believed. We have seen in the preceding examples that if we had had complete confidence in the prevailing theory of the destruction of sugar in animals, and if we had only had its confirmation in view, we should probably not have found the road to the new facts which we met. It is true that an hypothesis based on a theory produced the experiment; but as soon as the results of the experiment appeared, theory and hypothesis had to disappear, for the experimental facts were now just an observation, to be made without any preconceived idea.

In sciences as complex and as little developed as physiology, the great principle is therefore to give little heed to hypotheses or theories and always to keep an eye alert to observe everything that appears in every aspect of an experiment. An apparently accidental and inexplicable circumstance may occasion the discovery of an important new fact, as we shall see in the continuation of the example just noted.

SECOND EXAMPLE (Sequel to the last).   After finding, as I said above, that there is sugar in the livers of animals in their normal state, and with every sort of nutriment, I wished to learn the proportion of this substance and its variation in certain physiological and pathological states. So I began to estimate the sugar in the livers of animals placed in various physiologically defined circumstances. I always made two determinations of carbohydrate for the same liver tissue. But pressed for time one day, it happened that I could not make my two analyses at the same moment; I quickly made one determination just after the animal's death and postponed the other analysis till next day. But then I found much larger amounts of sugar than those which I got the night before with the same material. I noticed, on the other hand, that the proportion of sugar, which I had found just after the animal's death the night before, was much smaller than I had found in the experiments which I had announced as giving the normal proportion of liver sugar. I did not know how to account for this singular variation, got with the same liver and the same method of analysis. What was to be done? Should I consider two such discordant determinations as an unsuccessful experiment and take no account of them? Should I take the mean between these experiments? More than one experimenter might have chosen this expedient to get out of an awkward situation. But I disapprove of this kind of action for reasons which I have given elsewhere. I said, indeed, that we must never neglect anything in our observation of fact, and I consider it indispensable, never to admit the existence of an unproved source of error in an experiment and always to try to find a reason for the abnormal circumstances that we observe, Nothing is accidental, and what seems to us accident is only an unknown fact whose explanation may furnish the occasion for a more or less important discovery. So it proved in this case.

I wished, in fact, to learn the reason for my having found two such different values in the analysis of my rabbit's liver. After assuring myself that there was no mistake connected with the method of analysis, after noting that all parts of the liver were practically equally rich in sugar, there remained to be studied only the elapsed time between the animal's death and the time of my second determination. Without ascribing much importance to it, up to that time I had made my experiments a few hours after the animal's death; now for the first time I was in the situation of making one determination only a few minutes after death and postponing the other till next day, i.e., twenty-four hours later. In physiology, questions of time are always very important because organic matter passes through numerous and incessant changes. Some chemical change might therefore have taken place in the liver tissue. To make sure, I made a series of new experiments which dispelled every obscurity by showing me that liver tissue becomes more and more rich in sugar for some time after death. Thus we may have a very variable amount of sugar according to the moment when we make our examination. I was therefore led to correct my old determination and to discover the new fact that considerable amounts of sugar are produced in animals' livers after death. For instance, by forcibly injecting a current of cold water through the hepatic vessels and passing it through a liver that was still warm, just after an animal's death, I showed that the tissue was completely freed from the sugar which it contained; but next day or a few hours later, if we keep the washed liver at a mild temperature, we again find its tissue charged with a large amount of sugar produced after it was washed.

Once in possession of the first discovery that sugar is formed in animals after death as during life, I wished to carry my study of this singular phenomenon further; I was then led to find that sugar is produced in the liver with the help of an enzyme reacting on an amylaceous substance which I isolated and which I called *glycogenous matter*, so that I succeeded in proving in the most clear-cut way that sugar is formed in animals by a mechanism in every respect like the mechanism found in vegetables.

This second series of facts embodied results, which are also firmly acquired for science, and which have greatly advanced our knowledge of glycogenesis in animals. I have just very briefly told how these facts were discovered, and how they started with an experimental circumstance that was apparently inconsequential. I quote this case so as to prove that we must never neglect anything in experimental research, for every accident has a necessary cause. We must, therefore, never be too much absorbed by the thought we are pursuing, nor deceive ourselves about the value of our ideas or scientific theories; we must always keep our eyes open for every event, the mind doubting and independent, ready to study whatever presents itself and to let nothing go without seeking its reason. In a word, we must be in an intellectual attitude which seems para-

doxical but which, in my opinion, expresses the true spirit
of an investigator. We must have robust faith and not
believe. Let me explain myself by saying that in science
we must firmly believe in principles, but must question
formulæ; on the one hand, indeed, we are sure that determinism exists, but we are never certain we have attained
it. We must be immovable as to the principles of experimental science (determinism), but must not absolutely
believe in theories. The aphorism which I just uttered is
sustained by what we expounded elsewhere, to wit, that
for experimental science principles are in our mind, while
formulæ are external things. In practical matters, we are
indeed forced to tolerate the belief that truth (at least
temporary truth) is embodied in a theory or a formula. But
in scientific experimental philosophy those who put their
faith in formulæ and theories are wrong. All human science
consists in seeking the true formula and true theory. We are
always approaching it; but shall we ever find it completely?
This is not the place to go into an explanation of philosophic
ideas: let us return to our subject and pass on to a fresh
experimental example.

THIRD EXAMPLE.   About the year 1852, my studies led me
to make experiments on the influence of the nervous system
on the phenomena of nutrition and temperature regulation.
It had been observed in many cases that complex paralyses
with their seat in the mixed nerves are followed, now by
a rise and again by a fall of temperature in the paralyzed
parts. Now this is how I reasoned, in order to explain this
fact, basing myself first on known observations and then on
prevailing theories of the phenomena of nutrition and temperature regulation. Paralysis of the nerves, said I, should
lead to cooling of the parts by slowing down the phenomena
of combustion in the blood, since these phenomena are considered as the cause of animal heat. On the other hand,
anatomists long ago noticed that the sympathetic nerves
especially follow the arteries. So, thought I inductively, in
a lesion of a mixed trunk of nerves, it must be the sympathetic nerves that produce the slowing down of chemical

phenomena in capillary vessels, and their paralysis that then leads to cooling the parts. If my hypothesis is true, I went on, it can be verified by severing only the sympathetic, vascular nerves leading to a special part, and sparing the others. I should then find the part cooled by paralysis of the vascular nerves, without loss of either motion or sensation, since the ordinary motor and sensory nerves would still be intact. To carry out my experiment, I therefore sought a suitable experimental method that would allow me to sever only the vascular nerves and to spare the others. Here the choice of animals was important in solving the problem; for in certain animals, such as rabbits and horses, I found that the anatomical arrangement isolating the cervical sympathetic nerve made this solution possible.

Accordingly, I severed the cervical sympathetic nerve in the neck of a rabbit, to control my hypothesis and see what would happen in the way of change of temperature on the side of the head where this nerve branches out. On the basis of a prevailing theory and of earlier observation, I had been led, as we have just seen, to make the hypothesis that the temperature should be reduced. Now what happened was exactly the reverse. After severing the cervical sympathetic nerve about the middle of the neck, I immediately saw in the whole of the corresponding side of the rabbit's head a striking hyperactivity in the circulation, accompanied by increase of warmth. The result was therefore precisely the reverse of what my hypothesis, deduced from theory, had led me to expect; thereupon I did as I always do, that is to say, I at once abandoned theories and hypothesis, to observe and study the fact itself, so as to define the experimental conditions as precisely as possible. Today my experiments on the vascular and thermo-regulatory nerves have opened a new path for investigation and are the subject of numerous studies which, I hope, may some day yield really important results in physiology and pathology. This example, like the preceding ones, proves that in experiments we may meet with results different from what theories and hypothesis lead us to expect. But I wish to call more special attention to this third example, because it gives us an important lesson, to wit: without the original guiding hypothesis, the experimental fact which contradicted it would never have been perceived. Indeed, I was not the first experimenter to cut this part of the cervical sympathetic nerve in living animals. Pourfour du Petit performed the experiment at the beginning of the last century and discovered the nerve's action on the pupil, by starting from an anatomical hypothesis according to which this nerve was supposed to carry animal spirits to the eye. Many physiologists have since repeated the same operation, with the purpose of verifying or explaining the changes in the eye which Pourfour du Petit first described. But none of them noticed the local temperature phenomenon, of which I speak, or connected it with the severing of the cervical sympathetic nerve, though this phenomenon must necessarily have occurred under the very eyes of all who, before me, had cut this part of the sympathetic nerve. The hypothesis, as we see, had prepared my mind for seeing things in a certain direction, given by the hypothesis itself; and this is proved by the fact that, like the other experimenters, I myself had often divided the cervical sympathetic nerve to repeat Pourfour du Petit's experiment, without perceiving the fact of heat production which I later discovered when an hypothesis led me to make investigations in this direction. Here, therefore, the influence of the hypothesis could hardly be more evident; we had the fact under our eyes and did not see it because it conveyed nothing to our mind. However, it could hardly be simpler to perceive, and since I described it, every physiologist without exception has noted and verified it with the greatest ease.

To sum up, even mistaken hypotheses and theories are of use in leading to discoveries. This remark is true in all the sciences. The alchemists founded chemistry by pursuing chimerical problems and theories which are false. In physical science, which is more advanced than biology, we might still cite men of science who make great discoveries by relying on false theories. It seems, indeed, a necessary weakness of our mind to be able to reach truth only across a multitude of errors and obstacles.

What general conclusions shall physiologists draw from the above examples? They should conclude that in the present state of biological science accepted ideas and theories embody only limited and risky truths which are destined to perish. They should consequently have very little confidence in the ultimate value of theories, but should still make use of them as intellectual tools necessary to the evolution of science and suitable for the discovery of new facts. The art of discovering new phenomena and of noting them accurately should today be the special concern of all biologists. We must establish experimental criticism by creating rigorous methods of investigation and experimentation, which will enable us to define our observations unquestionably, and thus get rid of the errors of fact which are the source of errors in theory. A man who today attempted a generalization for biology as a whole would prove that he had no accurate feeling for the present state of the science. Today, the biological problem has hardly begun to be put; and, as stones must first be got together and cut, before we dream of erecting a monument, just so must the facts first be got together and prepared which are destined to create the science of living bodies. This rôle falls to experimentation; its method is fixed, but the phenomena to be analyzed are so complex that, for the moment, the true promoters of science are those who succeed in giving its methods of analysis a few principles of simplification or in introducing improvements in instruments of research. When there are enough quite clearly established facts, generalizations never keep us waiting. I am convinced that, in experimental sciences that are evolving, and especially in those as complex as biology, discovery of a new tool for observation or experiment is much more useful than any number of systematic or philosophic dissertations. Indeed, a new method or a new means of investigation increases our power and makes discoveries and researches possible which would not have been possible without its help. Thus researches as to the formation of sugar in animals could be made only after chemistry gave us reagents for recognizing sugar, which were much more sensitive than those we had before.

c. Discovery

The primary purpose of all research is obviously to find something out. Analysis of this act of discovery reveals numerous ways in which it can take place. Some discoveries, when related to the history of science, seem to have been almost inevitable —to have been "in the air" for years or generations before being made. This favorable climate has sometimes resulted in simultaneous discovery by several individuals. One famous example was the invention of the calculus by both Newton and Leibnitz, which was marked by bitterness and controversy among individuals and nations. Another, in which the protagonists exhibited the utmost friendliness and courtesy, was the promulgation of the theory of evolution by Darwin and Wallace. Other discoveries have come with total unexpectedness and, as we shall see, have opened up completely new avenues of research. There have been discoveries made prematurely—in his article on page 94, Dr. Conant emphasizes that "experimental discoveries must fit the time"—and some of them have resulted in personal tragedy. Most readers are familiar with the story of Ignaz Semmelweis, who discovered the cause of puerperal fever in the lying-in wards of the general hospital at Vienna; it was being carried by putrefaction on the hands of physicians coming from the dissecting room. He proved experimentally that a disinfectant, chlorinated water, could prevent the disease, but not until Lister's work on antisepsis was his contribution fully recognized. He died lonely and embittered from an infection of the finger that was identical with the disease now associated with this name.

The role of chance in scientific discovery has been enormous. The reader has already seen one famous case, in which Claude Bernard "happened to observe" the urine of rabbits that, for no reason connected with research, had not been fed. The literature of science abounds in such examples, a few of which are described in this article. But chance is never the predominant factor in discovery. The beginning scientist who hopes by luck alone to emulate Lavoisier or Faraday, or even lesser scientists, is directed to Pasteur's famous statement that "chance favors only the prepared mind." This is really at the heart of Beveridge's discussion.

W. I. B. Beveridge was educated at the University of Sydney and at Cambridge, and is a professor of animal pathology at Cambridge and a Fellow of Jesus College. "Chance" is a chapter from his unconventional but authoritative book on The Art of Scientific Investigation. It was written as a practical guide to research and has become well known and influential among professional scientists.

CHANCE

W. I. B. BEVERIDGE

*"Chance favours only those who know
how to court her."*—CHARLES NICOLLE

Illustrations

IT WILL BE SIMPLER to discuss the rôle of chance in research if we first consider some illustrative examples of discoveries in which it played a part.

Pasteur's researches on fowl cholera were interrupted by the vacation, and when he resumed he encountered an unexpected obstacle. Nearly all the cultures had become sterile. He attempted to revive them by sub-inoculation into broth and injection into fowls. Most of the sub-cultures failed to grow and the birds were not affected, so he was about to discard everything and start afresh when he had the inspiration of re-inoculating the same fowls with a fresh culture. His colleague Duclaux relates:

To the surprise of all, and perhaps even of Pasteur,

who was not expecting such success, nearly all these fowls withstood the inoculation, although fresh fowls succumbed after the usual incubation period.

This resulted in the recognition of the principle of immunisation with attenuated pathogens.

The most important method used in staining bacteria is that discovered by the Danish physician C. Gram. He described how he discovered the method fortuitously when trying to develop a double stain for kidney sections. Hoping to stain the nuclei violet and the tubules brown, he used gentian violet followed by iodine solution. Gram found that after this treatment the tissue was rapidly decolorised by alcohol but that certain bacteria remained blue-black. The gentian violet and iodine had unexpectedly reacted with each other and with a substance present in some bacteria and not others, thus providing not only a good stain but also a simple test which has proved of the greatest value in distinguishing different bacteria.

While engaged in studying the function of the pancreas in digestion in 1889 at Strasbourg, Professors von Mering and Minkowski removed that organ from a dog by operation. Later a laboratory assistant noticed that swarms of flies were attracted by the urine of the operated dog. He brought this to the attention of Minkowski, who analysed the urine and found sugar in it. It was this finding that led to our understanding of diabetes and its subsequent control by insulin.

The French physiologist, Charles Richet, was testing an extract of the tentacles of a sea anemone on laboratory animals to determine the toxic dose when he found that a small second dose given some time after the first was often promptly fatal. He was at first so astounded at this result that he could hardly believe that it was due to anything he had done. Indeed he said it was in spite of himself that he discovered induced sensitisation or anaphylaxis and that he would never have believed that it was possible. Another manifestation of the same phenomenon was discovered independently by Sir Henry Dale. He was applying serum to strips of involuntary muscle taken from guinea-pigs when he encountered one that reacted violently to the application of horse serum. Seeking an explanation of this extraordinary observation he found that that guinea-pig had some time previously been injected with horse serum.

It was the usual practice among physiologists to use physiological saline as a perfusion fluid during experiments on isolated frogs' hearts. By this means they could be kept beating for perhaps half an hour. Once at the London University College Hospital a physiologist was surprised and puzzled to find his frogs' hearts continued to beat for many hours. The only possible explanation he could think of was that it was a seasonal effect and this he actually suggested in a report. Then it was found that the explanation was that his laboratory assistant had used tap water instead of distilled water to make up the saline solution. With this clue it was easy to determine what salts in the tap water were responsible for the increased physiological activity. This was what led Sidney Ringer to develop the solution which bears his name and which has contributed so much to experimental physiology.

Gowland Hopkins, whom many consider the father of biochemistry, gave his practical class a certain well-known test for proteins to carry out as an exercise, but all the students failed to elicit the reaction. Investigation revealed that the reaction was only obtained when the acetic acid employed contained an impurity, glyoxylic acid, which thereafter became the standard test reagent. Hopkins followed up this clue further and sought the group in the protein with which the glyoxylic acid reacted, and this led him to his famous isolation of tryptophane.

It was not a physicist but a physiologist, Luigi Galvani, who discovered current electricity. He noticed twitchings of the muscles of frogs' legs hanging from an iron balustrade in his home in Bologna. Investigation revealed that twitching occurred when one part of the leg was in contact with iron and the other with a piece of copper wire attached at one end to the iron. From this observation he developed his metallic arc which led to the understanding of current electricity and the invention of the voltaic cell by Volta.

In 1822 the Danish physicist, Oersted, at the end of a lecture happened to bring a wire joined at its two extremities to a voltaic cell, to a position above and parallel to a magnetic needle. At first he had purposely held the wire perpendicular to the needle but nothing happened, but when by chance he held the wire horizontally and parallel to the needle he was astonished to see the needle change position. With quick insight he reversed the current and found that the needle deviated in the opposite direction. Thus by mere chance the relationship between electricity and magnetism was discovered and the path opened for the invention by Faraday of the electric dynamo. It was when telling of this that Pasteur made his famous remark: "In the field of observation chance favours only the prepared mind." Modern civilisation perhaps owes more to the discovery of electro-magnetic induction than to any other single discovery.

When von Röntgen discovered X-rays he was experimenting with electrical discharges in high vacua and using barium platinocyanide with the object of detecting invisible rays, but had no thought of such rays being able to penetrate opaque materials. Quite by chance he noticed that barium platinocyanide left on the bench near his vacuum tube became fluorescent although separated from the tube by black paper. He afterwards said: "I found by accident that the rays penetrated black paper."

When W. H. Perkin was only eighteen years old he tried to produce quinine by the oxidation of allyl-o-toluidine by potassium dichromate. He failed, but thought it might be interesting to see what happened when a simpler base was treated with the same oxidiser. He chose aniline sulphate and thus produced the first aniline dye. But chance played an even bigger part than the bare facts indicate: had not his aniline contained as an impurity some p-toluidine the reaction could not have occurred.

A mixture of lime and copper sulphate was sprayed on posts supporting grape vines in Medoc with the object of frightening away pilferers. Millardet later noticed that leaves accidentally sprayed with the mixture were free from mildew. The following up of this clue led to the important discovery of the value of Bordeaux mixture in protecting fruit trees and vines from many diseases caused by fungi.

The circumstances leading to the discovery of penicillin are widely known. Fleming was working with some plate cultures of staphylococci which he had occasion to open several times and, as often happens in such circumstances, they became contaminated. He noticed that the colonies of staphylococci around one particular colony died. Many bacteriologists would not have thought this particularly remarkable for it has long been known that some bacteria interfere with the growth of others. Fleming, however, saw the possible significance of the observation and followed it up to discover penicillin, although its development as a therapeutic agent was due to the subsequent work of Sir Howard Florey. The element of chance in this discovery is the more remarkable when one realises that that particular mold is not a very common one and, further, that subsequently a most extensive, world-wide search for other antibiotics has failed to date to discover anything else as good. It is of interest to note that the discovery would probably not have been made had not Fleming been working under "unfavorable" conditions in an old building where there was a lot of dust and contaminations were likely to occur.

J. Ungar found that the action of penicillin on certain bacteria was slightly enhanced by the addition to the medium of paraminobenzoic acid (PABA). He did not explain what made him try this out but it seems likely that it was because PABA was known to be an essential growth factor for bacteria. Subsequently, Greiff, Pinkerton and Moragues tested PABA to see if it enhanced the weak inhibitory effect which penicillin had against typhus rickettsiae. They found that PABA alone had a remarkably effective chemotherapeutic action against the typhus organisms. "This result was quite unexpected," they said. As a result of this work PABA became recognised as a valuable chemotherapeutic agent for the typhus group of fevers, against which previously nothing had been found effective.

Salvarsan and sulphanilamide were discovered following an hypothesis that was not correct. Two other equally famous chemotherapeutic drugs were discovered only because they happened to be present as impurities in other substances which were being tested. Scientists closely associated with the work have told me the stories of these two discoveries but have asked me not to publish them as other members of the team may not wish the way in which they made the discovery to be made public. Sir Lionel Whitby has told to me a story of a slightly different nature. He was conducting an experiment on the then new drug, sulphapyridine, and mice inoculated with pneumococci were being dosed throughout the day, but were not treated during the night. Sir Lionel had been out to a dinner party and before returning home visited the laboratory to see how the mice were getting on, and while there lightheartedly gave the mice a further dose of the drug. These mice resisted the pneumococci better than any mice had ever done before. Not till about a week later did Sir Lionel realise that it was the extra dose at midnight which had been responsible for the excellent results. From that time, both mice and men were dosed day and night when under sulphonamide treatment and they benefited much more than under the old routine.

In my researches on foot-rot in sheep I made numerous attempts to prepare a medium in which the infective agent would grow. Reason led me to use sheep serum in the medium and the results were repeatedly negative. Finally I got a positive result and on looking back over my notes I saw that, in that batch of media, horse serum had been used in place of sheep serum because the supply of the latter had temporarily run out. With this clue it was a straightforward matter to isolate and demonstrate the causal agent of the disease—an organism which grows in the presence of horse serum but not sheep serum! Chance led to a discovery where reason had pointed in the opposite direction.

The discovery that the human influenza virus is able to infect ferrets was a landmark in the study of human respiratory diseases. When an investigation on influenza was planned, ferrets were included among a long list of animals it was intended to try and infect sooner or later. However, some time before it was planned to try them, it was reported that a colony of ferrets was suffering from an illness which seemed to be the same as the influenza then affecting the people caring for them. Owing to this circumstantial evidence, ferrets were immediately tried and found susceptible to influenza. Afterwards it was found that the idea which prompted the tests in ferrets was quite mistaken for the disease occurring in the colony of ferrets was not influenza but distemper!

Scientists working on the technicalities of food preservation tried prolonging the "life" of chilled meat by replacing the air by carbon dioxide which was known to have an inhibitory effect on the growth of micro-organisms causing spoilage. Carbon dioxide, at the high concentration used, was found to cause an unpleasing discoloration of the meat and the whole idea was abandoned. Some time later, workers in the same laboratory were investigating a method of refrigeration which involved the release of carbon dioxide into the chamber in which the food was stored, and observations were carried out to see whether the gas had any undesirable effect. To their surprise the meat not only remained free from discoloration but even in the relatively low concentrations of carbon dioxide involved it kept in good condition much longer than ordinarily. From this observation was developed the important modern process of "gas storage" of meat in which 10–12 per cent carbon dioxide is used. At this concentration the gas effectively prolongs the "life" of chilled meat without causing discoloration.

I was investigating a disease of the genitalia of sheep known as balano-posthitis. It is a very long-lasting disease and was thought to be incurable except by radical surgery. Affected sheep were sent from the country to the laboratory for investigation but to my surprise they all healed spontaneously within a few days of arrival. At first it was thought that typical cases had not been sent, but further investigation showed that the self-imposed fasting of the sheep when placed in a strange environment had cured the disease. Thus it was found that this disease, refractory to other forms of treatment, could in most cases be cured by the simple expedient of fasting for a few days.

Paul Ehrlich's discovery of the acid-fast method of staining tubercle bacilli arose from his having left some preparations on a stove which was later inadvertently lighted by someone. The heat of the stove was just what was required to make these waxy-coated bacteria take the stain. Robert Koch said "We owe it to this circumstance alone that it has become a general custom to search for the bacillus in sputum."

Rôle of Chance in Discovery

These examples provide striking illustration of the important part that chance plays in discovery. They are the more remarkable when one thinks of the failures and frustrations usually met in research. Probably the majority of discoveries in biology and medicine have been come upon unexpectedly, or at least had an element of chance in them, especially the most important and revolutionary ones. It is scarcely possible to foresee a discovery that breaks really new ground, because it is often not in accord with current beliefs. Frequently I have heard a colleague, relating some new finding, say almost apologetically, "I came across it by accident." Although it is common knowledge that sometimes chance is a factor in the making of a discovery, the magnitude of its importance is seldom realised and the significance of its rôle does not seem to have been fully appreciated or understood. Books have been written on scientific method omitting any reference to chance or empiricism in discovery.

Perhaps the most striking examples of empirical discoveries are to be found in chemotherapy where nearly all the great discoveries have been made by following a false hypothesis or a so-called chance observation. Elsewhere are described the circumstances in which were discovered the therapeutic effects of salvarsan, sulphanilamide and penicillin. Subsequent rational research in each case provided only relatively small improvements. These facts are the more amazing when one thinks of the colossal amount of rational research that has been carried out in chemotherapy.

The research worker should take advantage of this knowledge of the importance of chance in discovery and not pass over it as an oddity or, worse, as something detracting from the credit due to the discoverer and therefore not to be dwelt upon. Although we cannot deliberately evoke that will-o'the-wisp, chance, we can be on the alert for it, prepare ourselves to recognise it and profit by it when it comes. Merely realising the importance of chance may be of some help to the beginner. We need to train our powers of observation, to cultivate that attitude of mind of being constantly on the look-out for the unexpected and make a habit of examining every clue that chance presents. Discoveries are made by giving attention to the slightest clue. That aspect of the scientist's mind which demands convincing evidence should be reserved for the proof stage of the investigation. In research, an attitude of mind is required for discovery which is different from that required for proof, for discovery and proof are distinct processes. We should not be so obsessed with our hypothesis that we miss or neglect anything not directly bearing on it. With this in mind, Bernard insisted that, although hypotheses are essential in the planning of an experiment, once the experiment is commenced the observer should forget his hypothesis. People who are too fond of their hypotheses, he said, are not well fitted for making discoveries.

A good maxim for the research man is "look out for the unexpected."

It is unwise to speak of luck in research as it may confuse our thinking. There can be no objection to the word when it is used to mean merely chance, but for many people luck is a metaphysical notion which in some mystical way influences events, and no such concept should be allowed to enter into scientific thinking. Nor is chance the only factor involved in these unexpected discoveries, as we shall discuss more fully

in the next section. In the anecdotes cited, many of the opportunities might well have been passed over had not the
workers been on the look-out for anything that might arise.
The successful scientist gives attention to every unexpected
happening or observation that chance offers and investigates
those that seem to him promising. Sir Henry Dale has aptly
spoken of opportunism in this connection. Scientists without
the flair for discovery seldom notice or bother with the unexpected and so the occasional opportunity passes without
them ever being aware of it. Alan Gregg wrote:

> One wonders whether the rare ability to be completely
> attentive to, and to profit by, Nature's slightest deviation
> from the conduct expected of her is not the secret of the
> best research minds and one that explains why some men
> turn to most remarkably good advantage seemingly
> trivial accidents. Behind such attention lies an unremitting
> sensitivity.

Writing of Charles Darwin, his son said:

> Everybody notices as a fact an exception when it is
> striking and frequent, but he had a special instinct for
> arresting an exception. A point apparently slight and un-
> connected with his present work is passed over by many
> a man almost unconsciously with some half considered
> explanation, which is in fact no explanation. It was just
> these things that he seized on to make a start from.

It is of the utmost importance that the rôle of chance be
clearly understood. The history of discovery shows that
chance plays an important part, but on the other hand it
plays only one part even in those discoveries attributed to
it. For this reason it is a misleading half-truth to refer to
unexpected discoveries as "chance discoveries" or "accidental
discoveries." If these discoveries were made by chance or
accident alone, as many discoveries of this type would be
made by any inexperienced scientist starting to dabble in
research as by Bernard or Pasteur. The truth of the matter
lies in Pasteur's famous saying: "In the field of observation,

chance favours only the prepared mind." It is the interpretation of the chance observation which counts. The rôle of chance is merely to provide the opportunity and the scientist has to recognise it and grasp it.

Recognising chance opportunities

In reading of scientific discoveries one is sometimes struck by the simple and apparently easy observations which have given rise to great and far-reaching discoveries making scientists famous. But in retrospect we see the discovery with its significance established. Originally the discovery usually has no intrinsic significance; the discoverer gives it significance by relating it to other knowledge, and perhaps by using it to derive further knowledge. The difficulties in the way of making discoveries in which chance is involved may be discussed under the following headings.

a] INFREQUENCY OF OPPORTUNITIES. Opportunities, in the form of significant clues, do not come very often. This is the only aspect affected by sheer chance, and even here the scientist does not play a purely passive rôle. The successful researchers are scientists who spend long hours working at the bench, and who do not confine their activities to the conventional but try out novel procedures, therefore they are exposed to the maximum extent to the risk of encountering a fortunate "accident."

b] NOTICING THE CLUE. Acute powers of observation are often required to notice the clue, and especially the ability to remain alert and sensitive for the unexpected while watching for the expected. Noticing is mainly a mental process.

c] INTERPRETING THE CLUE. To interpret the clue and grasp its possible significance is the most difficult phase of all and requires the "prepared mind." Let us consider some instances of failure to grasp opportunities. The history of discovery teems with instances of lost opportunities—clues noticed but their significance not appreciated. Before

Röntgen discovered X-rays, at least one other physicist had
noticed evidence of the rays but was merely annoyed.
Several people now recall having noticed the inhibition of
staphylococcal colonies by molds before Fleming followed
it up to discover penicillin. Scott, for instance, reports that
he saw it and considered it only a nuisance and he protests
against the view that Fleming's discovery was due to chance,
for, he says, it was due mainly to his perspicacity in seizing
on the opportunity others had let pass. Another interesting
case is related by J. T. Edwards. In 1919 he noticed that one
of a group of cultures of *Brucella abortus* grew much more
luxuriantly than the others and that it was contaminated
with a mold. He called the attention of Sir John M'Fadyean
to this, suggesting it might be of significance, but was
greeted with scorn. It was not till later that it was discovered that *Br. abortus* grew much better in the presence
of CO_2, which explains why Edwards' culture had grown
much better in the presence of the mold. Bordet and others
had casually noticed agglutination of bacteria by antisera,
but none had seen the possibilities in it until Gruber and
Durham did. Similarly, others had seen the phenomenon of
bacteriophage lysis before Twort and D'Herelle. F. M.
Burnet for one now admits having seen agglutination of
chick embryos' red blood cells in the presence of influenza
virus and probably others had too but none followed it up
till G. K. Hirst, and McClelland and Hare. Many bacteriologists had seen rough to smooth colony variation in
bacteria before Arkwright investigated it and found it to be
associated with change in virulence and antigenicity. It is
now, of course, one of the fundamental facts in immunology
and serology.

Anyone with an alertness of mind will encounter during
the course of an investigation numerous interesting side
issues that might be pursued. It is a physical impossibility
to follow up all of these. The majority are not worth following, a few will reward investigation and the occasional one
provides the opportunity of a lifetime. How to distinguish
the promising clues is the very essence of the art of research.
The scientist who has an independent mind and is able to

judge the evidence on its merits rather than in light of prevailing conceptions is the one most likely to be able to realise the potentialities in something really new. He also needs imagination and a good fund of knowledge, to know whether or not his observation is new and to enable him to see the possible implications. In deciding whether a line of work should be followed, one should not be put off it merely because the idea has already been thought of by others or even been tried without it leading anywhere. This does not necessarily indicate that it is not good; many of the classic discoveries were anticipated in this way but were not properly developed until the right man came along. Edward Jenner was not the first to inoculate people with cowpox to protect them against smallpox, William Harvey was not the first to postulate circulation of the blood, Darwin was by no means the first to suggest evolution, Columbus was not the first European to go to America, Pasteur was not the first to propound the germ theory of disease, Lister was not the first to use carbolic acid as a wound antiseptic. But these men were the ones who fully developed these ideas and forced them on a reluctant world, and most credit rightly goes to them for bringing the discoveries to fruition. It is not only new ideas that lead to discoveries. Indeed few ideas are entirely original. Usually on close study of the origin of an idea, one finds that others had suggested it or something very like it previously. Charles Nicolle calls these early ideas that are not at first followed up, "precursor ideas."

Exploiting opportunities

When a discovery has passed these hurdles and reached a stage where it is recognised and appreciated by its originator, there are still at least three more ways in which its general acceptance may be delayed.

d] FAILURE TO FOLLOW UP THE INITIAL FINDING. The initial disclosure may not be made the most of because it may not be followed up and exploited. The most productive scientists have not been satisfied with clearing up the immediate question but, having obtained some new knowledge, they made use of it to uncover something further and often of even greater importance. Steinhaeuser discovered in 1840 that cod-liver oil cured rickets but this enormously important fact remained unproved and no more than an opinion for the next eighty years. In 1903 Theobald Smith discovered that some motile bacilli may exist in culture as the normal motile form or as a non-motile variant, and he demonstrated the significance of these two forms in immunological reactions. This work passed almost unnoticed and was forgotten until the phenomenon was rediscovered in 1917 by Weil and Felix. It is now regarded as one of the fundamental facts in immunological reactions. Fleming described crude preparations of penicillin in 1929, but after a few years he dropped work on it without developing a therapeutic agent. He got no encouragement or assistance from others because they knew of many similar stories that had come to nothing. It was some years later that Florey took the work up from where·Fleming left off and developed penicillin as a therapeutic agent.

e]   LACK OF AN APPLICATION. There may be no possible applications of the discovery until years later. Neufeld discovered a rapid method of typing pneumococci in 1902, but it was not till 1931 that it became of any importance when type-specific serum therapy was introduced. Landsteiner discovered the human blood groups in 1901, but it was not till anticoagulants were found and blood transfusion was developed in the 1914–18 war that Landsteiner's discovery assumed importance and attracted attention.

f]   INDIFFERENCE AND OPPOSITION. Finally the discovery has to run the gauntlet of scepticism and often resistance on the part of others. This can be one of the most difficult hurdles of all ·and it is here that the scientist occasionally has to fight and in the past has sometimes even lost his life.

Several of the points discussed in this and the preceding section may be illustrated by narrating the story of Jenner's recognition of the potentialities of vaccination and his exploitation of it. Artificial immunisation against smallpox by means of inoculation with virulent smallpox material (variolation) had long been practised in the Orient. Some say that 1000 years B.C. it was the custom of China to insert material from smallpox lesions into the noses of children, others that variolation was introduced into China from India about A.D. 1000. Variolation was introduced from Constantinople into England about the middle of the eighteenth century and became an accepted though not very popular practice about the time that Edward Jenner was born. When Jenner was serving his apprenticeship between thirteen and eighteen years of age, his attention was called to the local belief in Gloucestershire that people who contracted cow-pox from cattle were subsequently immune to smallpox. Jenner found that the local physicians were mostly familiar with the traditional belief but did not take it seriously, although they also were encountering instances of failure of people to develop infection when given variolation after they had had cow-pox. Jenner evidently kept the matter in mind for years without doing anything about it. After returning to country practice he confided in a friend that he intended trying vaccination. He divulged his intentions under a bond of secrecy because he feared ridicule if they should fail. Meanwhile he was exercising his genius for taking pains and making accurate observation by carrying out experiments in other directions. He was making observations on the temperature and digestion of hibernating animals for John Hunter, experimenting with agricultural fertilisers for Joseph Banks and on his own behalf carrying out studies on how the young cuckoo gets rid of its fellow nestlings. He married at thirty-eight and when his wife had a child he inoculated him with swinepox and showed he was subsequently immune to smallpox. Still none of his colleagues—John Hunter among them—took much interest in Jenner's ideas about using cow-pox to vaccinate against smallpox and his first tentative paper on the subject was returned to him and apparently rejected. It was not till he was forty-seven years old (in the memorable year 1796) that he made his first successful vaccination from one human being to another. He transferred material from a pustule on the hand of a milkmaid, Sarah Nelmes, to an eight-year-old boy named James Phipps who thereby gained fame in the same odd way as did Joseph Meister for being the first person to receive Pasteur's treatment for rabies nearly a century later. This is taken as the classical origin of vaccination but, as is often the case in the history of scientific discovery, the issue is not clear-cut. At least two others had actually performed it earlier but failed to follow it up. Jenner continued his experiments, and in 1798 published his famous *Inquiry,* reporting some twenty-three cases who were either vaccinated or had contracted cow-pox naturally and were subsequently shown to be immune to smallpox. Soon afterwards vaccination was taken up widely and spread throughout the world, despite severe opposition from certain quarters which curiously and interestingly enough persists even today in a fairly harmless form. Jenner suffered abuse but honors were soon showered on him from all quarters of the globe.

This history provides an admirable demonstration of how difficult it usually is to recognise the true significance of a new fact. Without knowing the full history one might well suppose Jenner's contribution to medical science a very simple one not meriting the fame subsequently bestowed on it. But neither John Hunter nor any of Jenner's colleagues and contemporaries were able to grasp the potentialities in advance, and similar opportunities had occurred and been let pass in other countries. There was an interval of thirty years after the experimentally minded Jenner himself became interested in the popular belief, before he performed the classical, crucial experiments. With our present conceptions of immunisation and of experimentation this may appear surprising but we must remember how revolutionary the idea was, even given the fact that variolation was an accepted practice. The fact that others who had the same opportunity failed to discover vaccination and that it took Jenner thirty years shows what a difficult discovery it was to make. Animals were at that time regarded with repugnance by most people so the idea of infecting a human being with a disease of animals created utmost disgust. All sorts of dire results were prophesied, including "cow-mania" and "ox-faced children" (one was actually exhibited!). Like many great discoveries it did not require great erudition, and it mainly devolved on having boldness and independence of mind to accept a revolutionary idea and imagination to realise its potentialities. But Jenner also had practical difficulties to overcome. He found that cows were subject to various sores on the teats, some of which also affected the milkers but did not give immunity to smallpox. Even present day virus specialists have great difficulty in distinguishing between the different types of sores that occur on cows' teats, and there is no evidence available that any of them produce long lasting immunity in the cow.

Jenner's discovery has its element of irony which so often lends additional interest to scientific anecdotes. Modern investigators believe that the strains of vaccinia now used throughout the world for many years are not cow-pox but have derived from smallpox. Their origin is obscure but it seems that in the early days cow-pox and smallpox got mixed up and an attenuated strain of smallpox developed and was mistakenly used for cow-pox.

New knowledge very often has its origin in some quite unexpected observation or chance occurrence arising during an investigation. The importance of this factor in discovery should be fully appreciated and research workers ought deliberately to exploit it. Opportunities come more frequently to active bench workers and people who dabble in novel procedures. Interpreting the clue and realising its significance requires knowledge without fixed ideas, imagination, scientific taste, and a habit of contemplating all unexplained observations.

Mention has been made of the unexpected discovery that
results in a chain of related discoveries. The most noteworthy
example in modern science is the discovery of X rays by
Röntgen in 1895. Near the close of the nineteenth century,
many scientists believed that the major potentialities of physics
had been exhausted and that only minor refinements could
be expected. Röntgen's discovery and those that followed
in its train resulted in a revolution in previously existing
theories. The greater part of contemporary physics stems from
the discovery of this newly observed force in nature. As
Beveridge has pointed out, chance played a part in Röntgen's
discovery. "Chain Discoveries" describes its role in two
other major instances connected with the investigation of
radioactivity. The article thus serves a dual purpose: it illustrates the manner in which chain discoveries take place;
and it offers further evidence of the importance of chance
in scientific research.

René Taton is the author of numerous books and articles
on the history of mathematics, is a professor at the Sorbonne,
and is Secrétaire Général of the Union Internationale
d'Histoire et de Philosophie des Sciences. He has undertaken publication of a General History of Science, bringing
together the collaborations of a hundred authors, of which a
number of volumes have already appeared.

CHAIN DISCOVERIES

RENÉ TATON

AT CERTAIN EPOCHS the impetus of a new invention has
led to a whole series of quite different further discoveries
within a matter of years. Such examples of "associated discoveries" occur in the history of science quite often, for as
soon as an invention or a discovery of any importance, or
a somewhat spectacular hypothesis, concept or method opens

up new paths to science, many research workers will abandon their previous work and will be attracted to these new fields, into which they enter in the hope of gathering a new harvest of facts more quickly than they could have done elsewhere.

But the fruitful influence of an invention can equally appear in the form of a chain of discoveries of which each link is the more or less logical consequence of the preceding, and the cause of the subsequent one.

A particularly striking example of this type of discovery is found in the consequence of the discovery of X-rays by the German physicist Wilhelm Conrad Röntgen in November 1895, in his laboratory at Würzburg.

We shall first give a brief account of this discovery itself. Röntgen had long been interested in the cathode rays emitted by evacuated tubes, and while observing the flow of current in a Crookes's tube covered with black cardboard, he noticed the appearance of very clearly defined fluorescence on a screen of barium platinocyanide placed on the experimental table.[1] Surprised by this unexpected phenomenon, Röntgen made further experiments which established quite definitely that this fluorescence was caused by mysterious rays which, coming from the tube, had crossed the screen of black paper, despite the fact that this paper was opaque to all known forms of light. He then made a systematic study of this new radiation which, although invisible, could affect photographic plates and produce fluorescence in some substances, and which had a previously unheard-of power of penetration. At the time he could not specify the nature of this radiation, and therefore gave it the name of X-rays. These new rays caused conductivity in the gases through which they passed, discharged electrified bodies, were not deviated by electrical fields, and seemed to be propagated in a straight line similar to light, but without the classical phenomena of reflection, refrac-

1. Other investigators, such as Crookes, had already noticed similar phenomena, but without attaching any importance to them. It is Röntgen's essential merit that he appreciated the full importance of this unexpected phenomenon.

tion and diffraction. However, the most astonishing property of X-rays was unquestionably their extraordinary power of penetration, varying with the nature of the body through which they passed. In the course of one of his experiments, Röntgen observed that the rays crossed his hand and that owing to the difference in transparency between bones and flesh he could obtain an image of the bone structure, and also of the contours of the opaque flesh, on a screen or a photographic plate.

The new possibilities of photographing the invisible were so astonishing that the new discovery very quickly took root both amongst the public at large and amongst scientific circles, arousing intense curiosity in both. Scientists were particularly interested since Röntgen's experiments were very easily repeated by means of very simple material found in all electrical laboratories. Thus on the 20th January, 1896, Drs. Oudin and Barthélemy were able to submit a "photograph of the bones of the hand taken by means of Prof. Röntgen's X-rays" to the Paris Académie des Sciences.

While a great number of experiments led to an ever-increasing concern for applying X-rays to human pathology, and particularly to surgical diagnosis, physicists were busy with determining the precise conditions for producing the new rays and with investigating their properties. Röntgen himself demonstrated that X-rays are produced whenever a beam of cathode rays meets a solid obstacle, gave evidence of the influence of the degree of rarefaction of the gas contained in the generating tube on the properties of the X-rays generated, and made the first experiments on the reflection of the rays. In the meantime many other physicists discovered various properties of this mysterious radiation which seemed to be very similar to that produced by light rays.

Here we shall merely consider the most immediate consequences. We shall not emphasize either Von Laue's elegant experiment of diffraction by crystal gratings in 1912 which definitely established the wave-nature of X-rays, Bragg's reflection experiment, the study of the spectra of the rays which led to the enunciation of Moseley's Law (1913), or the study of the corpuscular properties of these new rays. However, we must mention the most important discovery of radioactivity which, although its principles were certainly quite independent of X-rays, is nevertheless a direct consequence of Röntgen's discovery. The factual connection between these two discoveries will serve to illustrate the creative potentialities unleashed by some hypotheses, even if they are partially incorrect.

It was Henri Poincaré who, on the 20th January, 1896, presented to the Académie des Sciences the radiographic negatives of Oudin and Barthélemy, and also the first details of Röntgen's discovery. He particularly stressed the fact that in the still very rudimentary equipment used by the German physicist, X-rays appeared where the cathode rays emitted by the Crookes's tube hit the wall of the tube. Since the glass of the tube was found to be fluorescent in that region under the effect of the cathode rays, Poincaré assumed that the two phenomena of fluorescence and of the emission of X-rays were interconnected. In fact this assumption was erroneous. Later observations showed that the two phenomena were independent of each other—but Poincaré's assumption had the great merit of leading to a discovery of incalculable scope, that of radioactivity.

An old fellow-pupil of Poincaré at the École Polytechnique and a member of the Académie des Sciences, Henri Becquerel, lecturer at the Museum, and following in the footsteps of his father, Edmund Becquerel (1820–1891), had been keenly concerned with the very marked phosphorescence of uranium compounds. Thus he was directly interested in Poincaré's remarks and, at the suggestion of this great physicist and mathematician, he began systematic research on the question whether some bodies that fluoresced or phosphoresced after previous exposure to light did not also emit radiation similar to that of X-rays produced in Crookes's tubes. Poincaré developed this idea in an article in the *Revue Génerale des Sciences* on the 20th January, 1896. The article was devoted to the problem of invisible photography, and Poincaré's contribution appeared side by side with that of Röntgen, and that of the very young physicist Jean Perrin who, at the time, was preparing for his doctorate.

Excited by this experimental project which might shed new light on the phenomena of phosphorescence which he had studied for so long, Henri Becquerel first investigated crystals of the double sulphate of potassium and uranium of which he had a vast collection. In his first experiments, he exposed to sunlight for four hours photographic plates carefully shielded from the light by thick black sheets of paper on which he had placed a grain of the uranium salt. Upon developing the plates on the same day, he was pleased to discover that an outline of the grain of the phosphorescent salt had appeared in the form of a dark smudge. Poincaré's hypothesis was apparently verified: the salt had emitted a radiation which, like X-rays, could affect a photographic plate across a screen that is opaque to light. Becquerel announced his first discovery on the 24th February, 1896.

A few days later, while making further experiments with improved arrangements, he took out those plates which he was going to use. These plates had been kept in a dark drawer in the immediate proximity of the uranium crystals. Since they had not previously been exposed to light this factor was apparently irrelevant to the subsequent experiments. Nevertheless, owing to scruples typical of his strict experimental method, Becquerel decided to make sure first of all whether the plates were perfectly intact. For this purpose he developed one of them and was astonished to observe the outlines of the uranium sulphate crystals. He then decided to repeat the experiment by placing some uranium salt next to a photographic plate away from all light. The result was conclusive and showed that, without being exposed to the rays of the Sun, the crystals had emitted a radiation which, crossing sheets of paper, plates of glass and even aluminium, could affect photographic plates. Without waiting to get to the source of this phenomenon, discovered on the 2nd March, Becquerel communicated the result of his experiments to the Académie des Sciences. He was then fully convinced that he had discovered a property of exceptional importance that was soon to revolutionize classical physics; i.e. natural radioactivity. Becquerel then made a deeper study of this phenomenon and tried to fathom its consequences, which, in fact, turned out to be much more far-reaching than he could have suspected. He soon discovered that no previous luminous excitation however far removed in time was involved, and found that there was no decrease in activity as a function of time. He also verified that many other uranium salts could be used for the experiment with equal effect, a fact which soon led him to suppose that this is a property characteristic of the element uranium, and not related, as he had first thought, to the phenomenon of phosphorescence. Nevertheless Becquerel still remained convinced that this "uranic radiation" was identical with X-rays. His subsequent discoveries that "uranic radiation" could render the air conductive, discharging those electrified bodies that it acted upon, could but reassure this eminent physicist, at least provisionally, that he was correct in his idea.

Soon afterwards many research workers made a careful analysis of the nature of this new radiation. The study of its composition, of its behavior in a magnetic field and of its absorption, clearly demonstrated its complex nature, but it was not until after the discovery of new elements (and particularly of radium, an element producing far greater intensity of radiation than uranium) that its three constituents could be isolated, studied and identified. This achievement is mainly due to the English physicist Ernest Rutherford, to Becquerel, and to Pierre and Marie Curie in the course of research work lasting from 1897 to 1903. Rutherford designated the three radiations in growing order of their penetrating power by the Greek letters alpha, beta and gamma.

Towards the end of 1897, at the instigation of Becquerel, new research work was undertaken by the talented young physicist Pierre Curie, lecturer at the École de Physique et Chimie, and by his young wife Marie Curie, to investigate whether this property of emitting the new radiation was characteristic of uranium alone, or if it also operated in other chemical elements. This involved a systematic study of the radiation possibilities of the principal known substances. Tackling this work under her husband's guidance, Marie Curie first made a most meticulous study of the characteristics of this property, carefully distinguishing it from other phenomena with very similar characteristics. She then showed how this activity could be measured by the degree of conductivity that it induced in the air. Her subsequent systematic research work led to her being able to demonstrate the existence of another element which, like uranium, also emitted radiation, namely thorium, and thus to her supplanting the new erroneous expression "uranic radiation" with the word "radioactivity," a phenomenon which was to become of increasing importance. Some months later she made the further and much more brilliant discoveries of the two new elements polonium and radium, whose radioactivity was respectively many hundred and many million times that of uranium.

Without entering here into the details of these significant discoveries which, in their turn, opened up immense new horizons to science both in the theoretical and in the applied sphere, we shall merely note some points which we consider essential aspects of the methodology of scientific research.

To begin with, it is incontestable that the discovery of radium and polonium led to that of radioactivity, and that this development can be considered as due both to logical and also to factual reasons. Furthermore, the isolation of these two elements, existing as they do in very small proportions in even the richest ores, could not have been effected without making use of their radioactive properties.

Although it is well known, it is perhaps not useless to recall the starting point of the research work which led Pierre and Marie Curie to the isolation of these two new elements. This is, in fact, a particularly brilliant example of the essential role which systematic observation plays in scientific discovery, once a sufficiently discerning mind knows how to take advantage of what are apparently discrepancies that a more superficial observer might have overlooked. In the course of her systematic investigation of all substances having radioactive properties, Marie Curie noticed that certain compounds of uranium, viz. the oxide (pitchblende) and a double phosphate of uranium and copper (chalcolite), were very much more intensely radioactive than their uranium and thorium content would have led one to suppose. Marie Curie fully realized the importance of this fact, which she interpreted courageously and shrewdly.

"This fact," she pointed out in a note to the Académie des Sciences, "is very remarkable and leads one to believe that these minerals may contain an element that is much more active than uranium."

The accuracy of this hypothesis was to lead Pierre and Marie Curie to the discovery of radium, but a great deal of perseverance was still needed. Not knowing any of the chemical properties of the substance to be isolated, the two scientists concentrated their attention on its only observable property, radioactivity. Thus they devised a method of separation which, within twenty years, was to lead to the identification of all the other natural radioactive elements. This method consisted of applying every known physical and chemical means for separating different elements to the very complex minerals contained in pitchblende, and then of conserving those fractions that were most radioactive. Thus they could progressively enrich the radioactivity of two solutions by means of the fractionation of the original mineral. The first of these solutions, which showed characteristic traces of bismuth, allowed them to tackle the preparation of a new simple radioactive element called polonium (1898) in honor of Marie Curie's country of birth. The second fraction, containing barium, also showed intense radioactivity and its spectroscopic analysis revealed the presence of another new element—radium (26th December, 1898), of which Pierre and Marie Curie managed to isolate some decigrams in the form of the chloride. This was many million times more radioactive than uranium. Although its preparation, particularly in the beginning, had been very arduous and complicated, its radioactive properties were so intense that many consequences of radioactivity that had previously been unobserved could now be demon-

strated easily. Having at their disposal this much more
powerful source, physicists could now begin to elucidate
the mechanism of radioactivity, and thus revise their
concept of the constitution of matter.

We must insist on another point, namely the exceptional
determination, the self-denial and the courageous patience
which these two scientists brought to bear on the very
delicate and difficult operations of separation under ex-
ceptionally precarious material conditions, and with very
expensive apparatus. In order to obtain some decigrams of
pure chloride of radium they had had to treat two tons of
pitchblende, and to make thousands of operations and
measurements. However, to their courage and confidence in
success which made them persevere in their very often un-
rewarding tasks, the Curies added a very keen sense of
method and scientific strictness. Furthermore, by uniting
their efforts, they increased their chances of success, since
their research work involved a profound knowledge of very
different physical and chemical methods, and here their
individual training, mental orientations and tendencies very
fortunately supplemented one another. Their achievement
not only crowned their genius and courage, but it also
stressed the ever more imperative need for the collaboration
between research workers with different specialities and
scientific backgrounds.

We have here restricted our attention to the two most
essential discoveries which derived directly from the observation of X-rays by Röntgen. It cannot be denied that this
discovery contributed to a revision of all the most important
chapters of physics and chemistry. But other and quite
independent factors have equally contributed to this revolution which took place at the end of the nineteenth century.
However, in extending our study further, we should seriously
risk limiting its scope.

The main fact which we have wished to illustrate is the
effective connection between these three striking discoveries.
If the separation of radium imperatively required the prior
demonstration of radioactivity in an already known substance, the discovery of this latter phenomenon was by no

means the logical consequence of the discovery of X-rays. The artificially logical connection between these two facts was introduced not by the true nature of the facts, but by Poincaré's inaccurate hypothesis. Thus we have yet another extremely convincing example of error as a source of discoveries.

Before leaving this example, we must finally emphasize the part that unforeseen phenomena have played in these three discoveries; i.e. the appearance of fluorescent spots on Röntgen's screen, the appearance of the image of uranium-salt crystals on the plates stored in Becquerel's drawer, the observation of abnormal radioactivity of some uranium minerals by Marie Curie. However, in none of these cases was it accidental and trivial effects, but observations made by research workers trying to pay attention to all aspects of reality as paradoxical as they might appear, that led to the investigations. In every case the investigator, by strict and fruitful scientific procedure, knew how to give an adequate interpretation so that his discovery could become a part of science. In this respect there are perhaps few better examples of the scientific method applied with strictness and perspicacity.

This book contains numerous examples of that most exciting moment in science, when a flash of inspiration leads to discovery. This moment of creation, this flowering of the imagination, is epitomized by the famous episode in which Archimedes is supposed to have sprung from his tub and run naked through the house shouting "Eureka, eureka!" The legend may be apocryphal, but its essential verity is attested by hundreds of similar episodes. Its very words echo over the centuries as Faraday cries ecstatically, "I see! I see!"; and Pasteur in the episode here described by Baker exclaims, "All is discovered!"

The usual explanation of this intuitive "seeing through" is to attribute it to genius and label it incomprehensible. In the last analysis, this explanation is correct. Psychology is as yet too young to understand why some people are creative and

others are not. Yet we do know something of the processes
that accompany the act. One of them is an inner compulsion,
an intense desire to know. Without it, says John R. Baker, a
research worker cannot hope to be creative—in fact he cannot
properly be called a scientist.

Born in 1900, Baker is an English biologist who has collaborated in research with J. B. S. Haldane. He is a Reader in
Cytology at Oxford and is the recipient of the Oliver Bird
Medal for his work on chemical contraception. He is the author
of Sex in Man and Animals and The Scientific Life, from
which "The Act of Discovery" is taken.

THE ACT OF DISCOVERY

JOHN R. BAKER

*Lernen wir träumen, meine Herren,
dann finden wir vielleicht die Wahr-
heit.*

KEKULÉ

THE WORD DISCOVERY is used in science with two meanings, though they are not always very distinct. On the one
hand a new phenomenon or object may be disclosed, such as
the penetrating powers of X-rays or a living specimen of
a fish belonging to a group previously thought to have
been extinct for millions of years: on the other a new
principle or theory may be formulated, as when structural
formulae were suggested in organic chemistry or the
theory of natural selection put forward as a partial cause of
evolution. Discoveries may usually thus be classified as
factual or theoretical. In most sciences the factual discoveries
are commonly made in the laboratory, but they originate in
ways which would be surprising in their diversity to people
who are not themselves concerned with scientific research.

Ideas for experiments occur unexpectedly to the scientist anywhere and at any time of day or night, often when he is thinking of something else. Chance observations which he makes in his laboratory may suggest quite new lines of investigation. Important factual discoveries probably arise more commonly from such sources as these, than from the rigid following-up of a comprehensive plan of campaign deliberately thought out by the scientist in advance. Theoretical discoveries are seldom produced to order while the sanguine scientist sits conveniently confronted with a blank sheet of paper: they generally originate, like ideas for new lines of research, when he is far from laboratory or study.

Whenever one is able to look into the mind of a discoverer at the moment of discovery, one sees that the finding out of unknown facts and the origin of great generalizations are not crudely mechanical processes, to be achieved by the efficient sorting of the cards in a card-index or the punctual study of pre-publication abstracts of other people's work. Ideas come in the most unpredictable way, and seldom when they are being sought. One distinguished scientist has told me that his new ideas often come during railway journeys, and several have mentioned the capacity of a hot bath to generate plans for new investigations or for theories to account for what is already known. In the case of Archimedes the startlingly sudden origin of his important hydrostatical concept following the immersion of his own body in his bath has perhaps misled people into assuming that he was thinking of himself as the body submerged, whose weight would lose by submersion as much as was equal to the weight of the bath-water displaced. It seems at least as likely that the bath was acting simply as a generator of ideas.

It need scarcely be said that whatever originates in the train or bus or bath or bed or whatever incalculable place it may be, must subsequently be subjected to the most searching analysis in the cold light of the laboratory; but the idea must come first. Let us watch a couple of ideas of the first magnitude coming into the mind of a great German chemist.

So long as people are still interested in the history of science the name of August Kekulé will be honored, above all for his introduction of structural formulae in organic chemistry and his theory of the constitution of the benzene ring. He was not actually the originator of the concept of valency, but he devised the method of writing down the formulae of organic compounds which has been universally accepted ever since, on account of its demonstrating so clearly the way in which atoms and groups of atoms are linked together. The mere knowledge that so many carbon atoms, so many hydrogen atoms, etc., enter into a molecule of a substance does not mean very much; but if anyone with chemical knowledge can see, as he can from a structural formula, how they are linked, he can instantly infer many of the properties of the substance.

Kekulé himself has told us how the inspirations came which gave such a great impetus to chemical research. He announced it in his speech in the Berlin Rathaus on 11th March 1890, when the German Chemical Society met there to do him honor on the occasion of the twenty-fifth anniversary of the publication of his theory of the chemical structure of benzene. After the delivery of speeches by notable German chemists and the reading of letters and telegrams in his honor from representatives of chemical societies in various parts of the world, Kekulé made a simple, modest speech in which he told how the two greatest discoveries of his life came to him.

He told how he lived at one time near Clapham Common, and how he often went to Islington to spend the evening with his friend Hugo Müller. One night the two friends had spent the evening together in this way, talking of many things, but mostly of their beloved chemistry. It was summer, and Kekulé went home on the outside of an omnibus. "I sank," he said, "into a reverie. The atoms flitted about before my eyes. I had always seen them in movement, these little beings, but I had never succeeded in interpreting the manner of their movement. That day I saw how two small ones often joined into a little pair; how a larger took hold of two smaller, and a still larger clasped three or even four of the small ones, and how all span round in a whirling round-dance. I saw how the larger ones formed a row and only at the end of the chain smaller ones trailed along.

"The cry of the conductor, 'Clapham Road,' woke me up from my reverie, but I occupied part of the night in putting at least sketches of these dream-products on paper. Thus originated the structure-theory."

It was particularly the formulation of the theory of the benzene ring that the assembly had met to commemorate, and Kekulé told how this discovery also came to him, a discovery on which one-half of organic chemistry is based and which has proved more fertile than any other discovery in making possible verifiable and true predictions about the properties of substances. Those who have not studied organic chemistry will scarcely be able to comprehend how Kekulé's theory of the structure of benzene revolutionized the subject. In its essence it was a very simple theory: the six carbon atoms of the molecule are arranged in a ring, each linked to the next. The idea of this ring-structure came to Kekulé in another of his reveries.

During his residence at Ghent, he was sitting writing his chemical text-book. "But it did not go well; my spirit was with other things. I turned the chair to the fireplace and sank into a half-sleep. Again the atoms flitted before my eyes." His imaginative eye, sharpened by repeated visions of a similar kind, could by this time distinguish large structures of complicated construction. He had seen rows of atoms linked together, but never yet rings: nor had anyone else. This is how the idea came to him: "Long rows, variously, more closely, united; all in movement, wriggling and turning like snakes. And see, what was that? One of the snakes seized its own tail and the image whirled scornfully before my eyes. As though from a flash of lightning I awoke; this time again I occupied the rest of the night in working out the consequences of the hypothesis."

Kekulé did not tell of these incidents simply for the sake of something to say; he was deliberately advising on how to make discoveries in science. "Let us learn to dream, gentlemen, then perhaps we shall find the truth", but almost

immediately he gave a warning against the publication of
the dreams until they had been put to the test of the intelligence when awake.

As the embryologist, Dalcq, has insisted, it is wrong to
consider sciences as constructions methodically erected
according to a thought-out design. "Like all human achievements, they are a fruit of life, and of progress in those
directions which happen, at a certain moment, to be favour-
able." One might add that those who contribute to science
are drawn to their work not by any bureaucratic scheming,
but by an imperious internal drive: if sufficient drive is
there, it will overcome almost all obstacles. Every time a
motorist speaks of an amp, a wireless enthusiast of a micro-
farad, or a sailor of degaussing, a famous scientist is being
commemorated who rose through sheer ability without the
aid of wealth at a time when it was much harder to rise
than it is today. To anyone with the intense desire to find
out that characterizes the research worker, any other life
is tame, whatever attractions it may hold for a different
type of person. A recent correspondent in "Nature" has
said that young scientists have sometimes concealed their
degrees in science in order to get well-paid administrative
jobs. He calls this "waste of material," but it may be suggested that this is quite the wrong comment. The men had
had a training in science, but it is clear that they were not
scientists; and the real waste would have occurred if some
one had not realized their deficiencies and had given them
posts in research laboratories. One discovers or invents because one has an internal urge to do so, unless the environ-
mental conditions make it impossible. Every help should be
given to people in all walks of life who have the genuine
urge. The help should be encouragement, facilities and a
reasonable livelihood. The man who wants the higher pay
of an administrative job should be dissuaded from occupying
a potential research worker's seat in the laboratory of a
scientific institution.

In an amusing advertisement in the "Daily Telegraph"
a firm of tool-manufacturers announce that they invent
tools because they like inventing tools. This gives the

impression of being one of the most truthful advertisements one has ever read: the inventor has an urge which is comparable to that of the discoverer. It is only genuine interest in a subject, and not the hope of reward, that can make a research worker accept willingly the continual rebuffs which he receives in his work. Continually things go wrong: repeatedly he discovers that weeks or months of hard work have been thrown away on a line that will lead nowhere, or some one else discovers the same thing without his knowing it, and it looks as though all the time he has spent on the subject had been wasted. The continual disappointments would cure all but the genuine natural investigator in a very short time of any desire to devote his life to research; he would be unlikely to get so far as experiencing the joy of even a very small discovery. The man who works for reward or fame would never be able to force himself to do all the "useless" reading in subjects not immediately connected with his research that is so often a genuine pleasure to the real scientist. He reads omnivorously when he is not using his hands in his laboratory, and he reads because he is interested. Much that he reads he will never use again: just every now and then a remembrance of something he read long ago throws light on his immediate problem: he has a new insight into his work. His wider reading is utterly different from that of the writer of a text-book: he need reject nothing because it seems irrelevant, and his wider reading—I am not referring here to his concentrated study of the literature obviously connected with his research—would seem sketchy to anyone who examined him on it. Meanwhile ideas are accumulating, and most of them will lead to nothing; a few, when he is lucky, to discovery.

Nothing but an intense interest in the subject as a whole —in things—could make a man work so long with so many rebuffs and read so much with so little hope of profiting directly. The youthful aspirant to fame, who reads of the honors showered on Pasteur, likes to think of himself as a great medical research worker. He forgets that Pasteur was no aspirant to fame, nor even interested at first in medicine. He was, like all great scientists, intensely absorbed

in the study of things. It is useless to desire to become a
research worker because one desires fame, and equally useless to do so because one thinks that one can serve the
community by scientific research. The man who has the urge
to find out serves the community indeed, culturally or
materially or both, if given the opportunity; but he does so
because he believes in the value of finding out the truth
about things. A man with no special talents for music might
as well say that he was going to compose a symphony because he owed it to the community, as one without the gifts
of the natural investigator undertake scientific research for
the same reason. No scientist can tell what he is going to
discover: a man might seek something comparable in its
beneficence to trichlormethane and end up with a substance
so potentially horrible as $\beta\beta$-dichlordiethylsulphide to his
credit.

The joy of discovery is a very real incentive to research,
despite the rareness of its realization. It is an error to suppose that the scientist is unemotional, or could succeed if
he were. The error has arisen through a misconception. The
absolute necessity that a scientist's findings shall not be
changed from objective truth in response to emotional urges
of any kind does not result in his becoming a particularly
unemotional person: whether a discoverer or anyone else is
pleased with a discovery has no effect on its validity. "I have
been working like a madman at Drosera," wrote Darwin to
Sir J. D. Hooker in reference to his study of insectivorous
plants, and a few days later, to the geologist, Lyell, "at the
present moment I care more about Drosera than the origin
of all the species in the world. . . . I am frightened and
astounded at my results." Kropotkin once wrote, "There are
not many jobs in human life equal to the joy of the sudden
birth of generalization. . . . He who has once in his life
experienced this joy of scientific creation will never forget
it." Kropotkin did not exaggerate, and what he wrote is
as applicable to factual as to theoretical discoveries. Let us
witness an authentic case of joy in factual discovery.

"All is discovered!" The first shock is such that the young
scientist cannot put his eye back to the instrument, but only

emits this scarcely articulate cry. He rushes from his laboratory into the corridor. Meeting there a laboratory assistant in physics, he insists on embracing him. The assistant is dragged off to hear an exuberant account of what has transpired.

It was Pasteur who spoke. At the age of 25, before he turned to medicine, he made a discovery which, with those of van't Hoff, laid the foundations of the branch of chemistry which is concerned with the actual shapes of the ultimate particles of chemical compounds in the three planes of space.

It was already known that solutions of the salts of tartaric acid (from grape-juice) have a special effect on light. Light reflected from glass, or any other light in which the waves vibrate in one plane instead of (as in sunlight) in all planes at random, is affected by a solution of one of these salts. The light emerges from the solution with the waves still all vibrating in one plane, but the plane is a different one: the plane of polarization has been rotated to the right. Pasteur's discovery was this. He found that when he evaporated a solution of a salt of an acid very closely allied to tartaric acid, two sorts of crystals were produced, differing only in the positions of certain of their surfaces, so that one kind might be called right-handed and the other left. One kind of crystal was a familiar one, the other quite new. Pasteur was able, with the aid of the microscope, to separate the right-handed from the left-handed crystals, though the differences were small and the possibility of the existence of such differences not previously envisaged. He dissolved each kind of crystal separately and passed a beam of polarized light through each solution.

What he saw was the cause of Pasteur's excitement. One solution changed the plane of vibration in the usual way, to the right: the other, made from the new kind of crystals, changed it to the opposite direction, to the left. Thus the symmetry of the crystals was correlated with the optical behavior of their solutions, and an insight was given into the structure in the three planes of space of the ultimate particles of which chemical compounds are formed.

The excitement and joy of making a discovery is known

to every research worker, though in Britain the expression of the emotion is more reserved, so that when our colleague discovers something and we play the part of the laboratory assistant in physics in the corridor, we avoid the necessity of being kissed. The emotion is there whether the discovery is big or small, whatever the nationality of the discoverer may be. Let us watch a very great British scientist making a very small discovery.

Alfred Russel Wallace, co-founder with Charles Darwin of the theory of evolution by natural selection, catches a new species of butterfly in the Moluccas. It is a particularly brilliant species of the genus Ornithoptera. "None but a naturalist," wrote Wallace, "can understand the intense excitement I experienced when I at length captured it. On taking it out of my net and opening the glorious wings, my heart began to beat violently, the blood rushed to my head, and I felt much more like fainting than I have done when in apprehension of immediate death. I had a headache the rest of the day, so great was the excitement produced by what will appear to most people a very inadequate cause."

The joy of a discovery, big or small, is shared by a scientist's colleagues. The enthusiasm is infectious. Pasteur's crystallographic discovery illustrates the fact very pleasantly. He asked the old French chemist, Biot, for permission to demonstrate his results to him. Biot agreed, insisting that his own materials should be used and the test made in his own laboratory. The solution was made and allowed to evaporate for a couple of days. When sufficient crystals had appeared, Biot called Pasteur once more to his laboratory and in the former's presence the young scientist separated the right-handed crystals one by one from the left-handed. Biot dissolved them and decided first to examine the solution which should, according to Pasteur, rotate polarized light to the left. This was the solution of the new kind of crystal, with hitherto unexpected optical properties. Biot called Pasteur once more to his laboratory and proceeded to observe the effect on polarized light. He knew at once that a great discovery had been made. He seized Pasteur's arm and exclaimed, "My dear child, I have loved science so much in my life that that makes my heart throb."

It was the sudden birth of a generalization—a theoretical discovery—that Kropotkin held to be so particularly joyful. Pasteur's discovery was factual, but not less satisfying for that. Kekulé's reveries resulted in theoretical discoveries. We may attend with advantage at the birth of another theoretical discovery, this time in biology, as important for science and as satisfying to its maker as Kekulé's.

Wallace himself regarded his work in describing and working out the distribution of the insects which he collected in the East Indies as incompletely satisfying or "comparatively profitless," as he expressed it. We should realize that he was comparing the "profit" with that of his great work on evolution by natural selection. The circumstances under which the great generalization was born in Wallace's mind are known. To Charles Darwin—originator of the phrase "natural selection"—the same great generalization came very slowly: upon Wallace, to use his own expression, it "flashed." One is reminded of Kekulé's comparison with a flash of lightning, when he conceived the structure of the benzene ring. Wallace and Darwin discovered independently the theory of a cause of evolution which is still, in an improved form, the most widely held today and has been a great stimulus to research.

Wallace was in his bungalow in the little island of Ternate in the Moluccas, his headquarters for the study of the fauna of the East Indies. Here, amid all the treasures of natural history that he had collected, the great naturalist was taking an enforced holiday as a result of repeated attacks of malarial fever. It was during an actual attack of fever that the idea came to him. His mind was reflecting on Malthus's "Principles of Population," and he brought his remembrance of this book, which he had read twelve years before, into connexion with the vast stores of knowledge that he had gained of the lives of wild animals in their native haunts in the East Indies. It was a supreme example of the value of wide reading to research workers. The principle of the survival of the fittest "suddenly flashed" upon him. "Then at once,"

he wrote, "I seemed to see the whole effect of this," and he
waited impatiently for his fit of fever to leave him, so that
he could write down a sketch of his theory. That same
evening he did so, and during the next two evenings he
wrote out a fuller account to send to Darwin.

The scientist would be a self-centered person if he cared
nothing for the good opinion of his colleagues. It is not
fame that he wants, for that would mean that he respected
a value set upon his work by those who could not be in
a position to assess it truly. The good opinion of colleagues
is desired by nearly every research worker, and when it is
gained—and it can only be gained by the revelation of
demonstrable truth—there is a satisfaction as great as and
perhaps more lasting than the initial joy in discovery, a
satisfaction all the more real because others can take genuine
unselfish pleasure, like Biot, in the discovery. Ray Lankester
expressed these feelings very directly when he gave an
account of the first known fresh-water jelly-fish.

One Thursday in the summer of 1880 the Secretary of
the Botanical Society of London noticed some strange
organisms floating in a warm-water tank, in the house in
Regent's Park devoted to the cultivation of the magnificent
water-lily, Victoria regia. By the following Monday he had
placed a number of specimens at Lankester's disposal. The
organisms were jelly-fish. Never previously had a jelly-fish
(Medusa) been known to inhabit fresh water: the kinds of
animals popularly so called were thought by the best scientific opinion of the time to be exclusively marine. Lankester
wasted no time; nor did Allman, another distinguished
zoologist, to whom the Secretary also gave some specimens.
On the Thursday morning, just one week from the time the
organism was first seen, a description of it by Lankester was
already in print, and on the same afternoon Allman was
describing it at the Linnean Society. (By the inflexible law
of priority, Lankester's name of Craspedacusta was accepted
for the animal in preference to Allman's Limnocodium,
though Lankester, with a somewhat Irish gesture, tried
simultaneously to change his name into a philologically more
exact form and to withdraw it altogether out of respect for

Allman.) A week later quite a long paper on the physiology of the new animal was already published by the celebrated biologist whose memory is kept fresh in Oxford by the Romanes lectures, still delivered annually on scientific or literary topics. On the same day Lankester wrote: "I confess to having worked at that Medusa day and night when I first obtained it, with the object of having the pleasure and honor of being the first to expound its structure to my brother naturalists."

Lankester referred to the pleasure and honour of his work; Darwin in his autobiography put love of science first in the list of the mental qualities which gave him success in research. It may be left to a philosopher to describe more particularly the value of science to the scientist. The pleasure of science, as Alexander says, "is sometimes felt passionately, most often it is a calm delight in contemplating the harmonies of knowledge. It may be attended by subsidiary excitements in the work of investigation, some of which are pleasureable in so far as the labour tends to success; others involve pain or suspense. The release from such tension, when disappointment and frustration are replaced by discovery, adds a glow to the exercise of the search. . . . Truth is the satisfaction of disinterested curiosity."

For John Livingston Lowes, the act of imaginative creation is fundamentally the same in science and in art. He sees three factors at work which he labels the Well, the Vision, and the Will. He likens the Ancient Mariner of Coleridge to the theories of Darwin and Newton and discusses how the three factors played their roles in the achievements of all three men. A professor of English at Harvard and a visiting professor at Oxford, Lowes was a man of encyclopedic learning. He specialized in the critical study of Chaucer, Milton, and Coleridge. "Imagination Creatrix" is an excerpt from his brilliant book The Road to Xanadu. He died in 1945.

IMAGINATION CREATRIX

JOHN LIVINGSTON LOWES

I

EVERY GREAT IMAGINATIVE CONCEPTION is a vortex into which everything under the sun may be swept. "All other men's worlds," wrote Coleridge once, "are the poet's chaos." In that regard "The Ancient Mariner" is one with the noble army of imaginative masterpieces of all time. Oral traditions —homely, fantastic, barbaric, disconnected—which had ebbed and flowed across the planet in its unlettered days, were gathered up into that marvel of constructive genius, the plot of the *Odyssey*, and out of "a tissue of old *märchen*" was fashioned a unity palpable as flesh and blood and universal as the sea itself. Well-nigh all the encyclopedic erudition of the Middle Ages was forged and welded, in the white heat of an indomitable will, into the steel-knot structure of the *Divine Comedy*. There are not in the world, I suppose, more appalling masses of raw fact than would stare us in the face could we once, through some super-subtle chemistry, resolve that superb, organic unity into its primal elements. It so happens that for the last twenty-odd years I have been more or less occupied with Chaucer. I have tracked him, as I have trailed Coleridge, into almost every section of eight floors of a great library. It is a perpetual adventure among uncharted Ophirs and Golcondas to read after him—or Coleridge. And every conceivable sort of thing which Chaucer knew went into his alembic. It went in *x*—a waif of travel-lore from the mysterious Orient, a curious bit of primitive psychiatry, a racy morsel from Jerome against Jovinian, alchemy, astrology, medicine, geomancy, physiognomy, Heaven only knows what not, all vivid with the relish of the reading—it went in stark fact, "nude and crude," and it came out pure Chaucer. The results are as different from "The Ancient Mariner" as an English post-road from spectre-haunted seas. But the basic operations which produced them (and on this point I may venture to speak from first-hand knowledge) are essentially the same.

As for the years of "industrious and select reading, steady observation, insight into all seemly and generous arts and affairs" which were distilled into the magnificent romance of the thunder-scarred yet dauntless Rebel, voyaging through Chaos and old Night to shatter Cosmos, pendent from the battlements of living sapphire like a star—as for those serried hosts of facts caught up into the cosmic sweep of Milton's grandly poised design, it were bootless to attempt to sum up in a sentence here the opulence which countless tomes of learned comment have been unable to exhaust. And what (in apostolic phrase) shall I more say? For the time would fail me to tell of the *Æneid,* and the *Orlando Furioso,* and the *Faërie Queene,* and *Don Juan,* and even *Endymion,* let alone the cloud of other witnesses. The notion that the creative imagination, especially in its highest exercise, has little or nothing to do with facts is one of the *pseudodoxia epidemica* which die hard.

For the imagination never operates in a vacuum. Its stuff is always fact of some order, somehow experienced; its product is that fact transmuted. I am not forgetting that facts may swamp imagination, and remain unassimilated and untransformed. And I know, too, that this sometimes happens even with the masters. For some of the greatest poets, partly by virtue of their very greatness, have had, like Faust, two natures struggling within them. They have possessed at once the instincts of the scholar and the instincts of the artist, and it is precisely with regard to facts that these instincts perilously clash. Even Dante and Milton and Goethe sometimes clog their powerful streams with the accumulations of the scholar who shared bed and board with the poet in their mortal frames. "The Professor still lurks in your anatomy"—*Dir steckt der Doktor noch im Leib*—says Mephistopheles to Faust. But when, as in

"The Ancient Mariner," the stuff that Professors and Doctors are made of has been distilled into quintessential poetry, then the passing miracle of creation has been performed.

II

But "creation," like "creative," is one of those hypnotic words which are prone to cast a spell upon the understanding and dissolve our thinking into haze. And out of this nebulous state of the intellect springs a strange but widely prevalent idea. The shaping spirit of imagination sits aloof, like God as he is commonly conceived, creating in some thaumaturgic fashion out of nothing its visionary world. That and that only is deemed to be "originality"—that, and not the imperial molding of old matter into imperishably new forms. The ways of creation are wrapt in mystery; we may only marvel, and bow the head.

Now it is true beyond possible gainsaying that the operations which we call creative leave us in the end confronting mystery. But that is the fated terminus of all our quests. And it is chiefly through a deep-rooted reluctance to retrace, so far as they are legible, the footsteps of the creative faculty that the power is often thought of as abnormal, or at best a splendid aberration. I know full well that this reluctance springs, with most of us, from the staunch conviction that to follow the evolution of a thing of beauty is to shatter its integrity and irretrievably to mar its charm. But there are those of us who cherish the invincible belief that the glory of poetry will gain, not lose, through a recognition of the fact that the imagination works its wonders through the exercise, in the main, of normal and intelligible powers. To establish that, without blinking the ultimate mystery of genius, is to bring the workings of the shaping spirit in the sphere of art within the circle of the great moulding forces through which, in science and affairs and poetry alike, there emerges from chaotic multiplicity a unified and ordered world.

Creative genius, in plainer terms, works through processes which are common to our kind, but these processes are superlatively enhanced. The subliminal agencies are endowed with an extraordinary potency; the faculty which conceives and executes operates with sovereign power; and the two blend in untrammelled interplay. There is always in genius, I imagine, the element which Goethe, who knew whereof he spoke, was wont to designate as "the Dæmonic." But in genius of the highest order that sudden, incalculable, and puissant energy which pours up from the hidden depths is controlled by a will which serves a vision—the vision which sees in chaos the potentiality of Form.

III

. . . "The imagination," said Coleridge once, recalling a noble phrase from Jeremy Taylor's *Via Pacis*, ". . . *sees all things in one.*" It sees the Free Life—the endless flux of the unfathomed sea of facts and images—but it sees also the controlling Form. And when it acts on what it sees, through the long patience of the will the flux itself is transformed and fixed in the clarity of a realized design. For there enter into imaginative creation three factors which reciprocally interplay: the Well, and the Vision, and the Will. Without the Vision, the chaos of elements remains a chaos, and the Form sleeps forever in the vast chambers of unborn designs. Yet in *that* chaos only could creative Vision ever see *this* Form. Nor without the cooperant Will, obedient to the Vision, may the pattern perceived in the huddle attain objective reality. Yet manifold though the ways of the creative faculty may be, the upshot is one: from the empire of chaos a new tract of cosmos has been retrieved; a nebula has been compacted—it may be!—into a star.

Yet no more than the lesser are these larger factors of the creative process—the storing of the Well, the Vision, and the concurrent operation of the Will—the monopoly of poetry. Through their conjunction the imagination in the field of science, for example, is slowly drawing the immense confusion of phenomena within the unfolding conception of an ordered universe. And its operations are essentially the same. For years, through intense and unremitting observation, Darwin had been accumulating masses of facts which pointed to a momentous conclusion. But they pointed through a maze of baffling inconsistencies. Then all at once the flash of vision came. "I can remember," he tells us in that precious fragment of an autobiography—"I can remember the very spot in the road, whilst in my carriage, when to my joy the solution occurred to me." And then, and only then, with the infinite toil of exposition, was slowly framed from the obdurate facts the great statement of the theory of evolution. The leap of the imagination, in a garden at Woolsthorpe on a day in 1665, from the fall of an apple to an architectonic conception cosmic in its scope and grandeur is one of the dramatic moments in the history of human thought. But in that pregnant moment there flashed together the profound and daring observations and conjectures of a long period of years; and upon the instant of illumination followed other years of rigorous and protracted labor, before the *Principia* appeared. Once more there was the long, slow storing of the Well; once more the flash of amazing vision through a fortuitous suggestion; once more the exacting task of translating the vision into actuality. And those are essentially the stages which Poincaré observed and graphically recorded in his "Mathematical Discovery." And that chapter reads like an exposition of the creative processes through which "The Ancient Mariner" came to be. With the inevitable and obvious differences we are not here concerned. But it is of the utmost moment to more than poetry that instead of regarding the imagination as a bright but ineffectual faculty with which in some esoteric fashion poets and their kind are specially endowed, we recognize the essential oneness of its function and its ways with all the creative endeavors through which human brains, with dogged persistence, strive to discover and realize order in a chaotic world.

For the Road to Xanadu is the road of the human spirit, and the imagination voyaging through chaos and reducing it to clarity and order is the symbol of all the quests which lend glory to our dust. And the goal of the shaping spirit which hovers in the *poet's* brain is the clarity and order of pure beauty. Nothing is alien to its transforming touch "Far or forgot to (it) is near; Shadow and sunlight are the same." Things fantastic as the dicing of spectres on skeleton-barks, and ugly as the slimy spawn of rotting seas, and strange as a star astray within the moon's bright tip, blend in its vision into patterns of new-created beauty, *herrlich, wie am ersten Tag.* Yet the pieces that compose the pattern are not new. In the world of the shaping spirit, save for its patterns, there is nothing new that was not old. For the work of the creators is the mastery and transmutation and re-ordering into shapes of beauty of the given universe within us and without us. The shapes thus wrought are not that universe; they are "carved with figures strange and sweet, All made out of the carver's brain." Yet in that brain the elements and shattered fragments of the figures already lie, and what the carver-creator sees, implicit in the fragments, is the unique and lovely Form.

One of the most extraordinary examples from science of the workings of the subconscious mind is described below by a Nobel Laureate in medicine. Isaac Newton once stated that he solved problems in science by always thinking into them. Loewi's case is more interesting psychologically because he verified a hunch after a period of seventeen years and without conscious thinking during the interim. There are of course other examples of a like nature, though perhaps none so dramatic. W. B. Cannon, the Harvard physiologist, wrote that he was accustomed to wake up in the morning with solutions to problems he had previously encountered. The process was so habitual that it became part of his regular research technique; and he was surprised when he discovered that others did not possess the same ability.

Loewi was born at Frankfort-on-Main, Germany, in 1873, and was a professor of pharmacology at the University of Graz, Austria, from 1909 to 1938. He was imprisoned by the Nazis and all his property confiscated; but was released and came to the United States in 1940, where he became a research professor at the New York University College of Medicine. A distinguished authority on metabolism, he also was profoundly interested in art, literature, and music. He died in 1961.

THE NIGHT PROWLER

OTTO LOEWI

THE BEST KNOWN of my scientific achievements was the establishment in 1921 of the chemical theory of the transmission of the nervous impulse. Until 1921 it was generally assumed that transmission was due to the direct spreading of the electrical wave accompanying the propagated nervous impulse from the nerve terminal to the effector organ. Since the character of that potential is everywhere the same, such an assumption would not explain the well-known fact that the stimulation of certain nerves increases the function of one organ and decreases the function of another. A different mode of transmission had, therefore, to be considered.

As far back as 1903, I had discussed with Walter M. Fletcher from Cambridge, England, then an associate in Marburg, the fact that certain drugs mimic the augmentary as well as the inhibitory effects of the stimulation of sympathetic and/or parasympathetic nerves on their effector organs. During this discussion, the idea occurred to me that the terminals of those nerves might contain chemicals, that stimulation might liberate them from the nerve terminals, and that these chemicals might in turn transmit the nervous impulse to their respective effector organs. At that time I did not see a way to prove the correctness of this hunch, and it entirely slipped my conscious memory until it emerged again in 1920.

The night before Easter Sunday of that year, I awoke, turned on the light, and jotted down a few notes on a tiny slip of thin paper. Then I fell asleep again. It occurred to me at six o'clock in the morning that during the night I had written down something most important, but I was unable to decipher the scrawl. The next night, at three o'clock, the idea returned. It was the design of an experiment to determine whether or not the hypothesis of chemical transmission that I had uttered seventeen years ago was correct. I got up immediately, went to the laboratory, and performed a simple experiment on a frog heart according to the nocturnal design. I have to describe briefly this experiment since its results became the foundation of the theory of chemical transmission of the nervous impulse.

The hearts of two frogs were isolated, the first with its nerves, the second without. Both hearts were attached to Straub canulas [laboratory tubes] filled with a little Ringer solution [a mixture of salts resembling blood plasma]. The vagus nerve [which regulates the heartbeat] of the first heart was stimulated for a few minutes. Then the Ringer solution that had been in the first heart during the stimulation of the vagus was transferred to the second heart. The second heart slowed and its beats diminished just as if its vagus had been stimulated. Similarly, when the accelerator nerve was stimulated and the Ringer from this period transferred, the second heart speeded up and its beats increased. These results unequivocally proved that the nerves do not influence the heart directly but liberate from their terminals specific chemical substances which, in their turn, cause the well-known modifications of the function of the heart characteristic of the stimulation of its nerves.

The story of this discovery shows that an idea may sleep for decades in the unconscious mind and then suddenly return. Further, it indicates that we should sometimes trust a sudden intuition without too much skepticism. If I had carefully considered it in the daytime, I would undoubtedly have rejected the kind of experiment I performed. It would have seemed likely that any transmitting agent released by a nervous impulse would be in an amount just sufficient to influence the effector organ. It would seem improbable that an excess that could be detected would escape into the fluid which filled the heart. It was good fortune that at the moment of the hunch I did not think but acted.

For many years this nocturnal emergence of the design of the crucial experiment to check the validity of a hypothesis uttered seventeen years before was a complete mystery. My interest in that problem was revived about five years ago by a discussion with the late Ernest Kris, a leading psychoanalyst. A short time later I had to write my bibliography, and glanced over all the papers published from my laboratory. I came across two studies made about two years before the arrival of the nocturnal design in which, also in search of a substance given off from the heart, I had applied the technique used in 1920. This experience, in my opinion, was an essential preparation for the idea of the finished design. In fact, the nocturnal concept represented a sudden association of the hypothesis of 1903 with the method tested not long before in other experiments. Most so-called "intuitive" discoveries are such associations suddenly made in the unconscious.

It has by now been made evident that scientific research, far from being the coldly logical activity which the uninitiated usually consider it, is in fact chancy, haphazard, and sometimes completely irrational. The history of science is studded with false starts and missed or bumbled opportunities. Sometimes such accidents of scientific progress have had profound repercussions. One of the most important in human history is here recorded by William L. Laurence, science reporter for The New York Times. Laurence was among the first to make public announcement of the fact that atomic fission had taken place under controlled experimental conditions. He was on the warplane that released the atomic bomb over Nagasaki and wrote an eyewitness account of the explosion. He is the recipi-

ent of numerous distinguished awards in journalism. There is
no reason to doubt his estimate of the situation he describes.
Such a sequence of events poses a fascinating and frightening
possibility for the future.

THE MIRACLE THAT SAVED THE WORLD

WILLIAM L. LAURENCE

THERE IS AN ANCIENT TALE about three princes of
Serendip who in their travels were always discovering, by
chance or by wisdom, things they did not seek. In allusion
to this tale, Horace Walpole coined the word "serendipity,"
meaning "the gift of finding valuable or agreeable things
not sought for."

The discovery of nuclear fission is the most famous modern
example of a discovery of tremendous importance—perhaps
the greatest in recorded history—made by serendipity. Here,
the minds of the original discoverers, and of many others
who continued their explorations, were completely unprepared. And here once again it was the case of preconceived ideas that blocked the recognition of revolutionary
facts.

As we shall presently relate, this unpreparedness on the
part of many of the world's most brilliant minds was, indeed, very fortunate for mankind's future. The world does
not yet realize—and it is recorded here for the first time—
the vital role that this unprecedented manifestation of collective intellectual blindness played in the preservation of
all the cherished values of Western civilization.

For had it not been for this collective intellectual blindness, Hitler would have had the atom bomb at the beginning
of World War II, and it is practically certain that he would
have been the only one to possess it.

The fact of the matter is that the splitting of the uranium

atom, which made the atomic bomb possible, first took place in the spring of 1934, more than five years before the beginning of World War II. It was done at the University of Rome. And the head of the team that split the uranium atom was none other than Enrico Fermi.

But according to all the laws of physics universally accepted at the time, there was no power on earth that could split an atom. None of the world's most illustrious physicists, including Einstein, Planck, Rutherford and Bohr, believed that it would ever be possible to split an atom. So Fermi and his brilliant team watched uranium atoms being split and failed to recognize what they saw.

For nearly five years brilliant nuclear physicists and nuclear chemists in many lands, including Irène Joliot-Curie, Nobel Prize-winning daughter of the famous Marie and Pierre Curie, discoverers of radium and polonium, repeated the Fermi experiments with uranium thousands of times. They all saw the same phenomena, which, had their minds been prepared, they could not have failed to recognize as the results of the splitting of the uranium atom into two lighter elements, accompanied by the release of vast quantities of nuclear energy. But so great is the power of preconceived ideas, even when false, that they failed to arrive at the only logical conclusion that could have explained what was happening before their eyes.

One shudders to think how close the world came to disaster in those days when young Fermi and his small crew of four—Eduardo Amaldi, Oscar d'Agostino, Franco Rasetti and Emilio Segré—stood gazing in wonder at a brood of strange products created in their crucible following their bombardment of a tiny amount of uranium with their neutron gun, a glass tube barely more than half an inch long from which neutrons streamed, knocked out from beryllium atoms by powerful nuclear "bullets" from radium. Had they become aware of what was actually taking place in their rather simple experimental chamber, the secret of the atomic bomb, and of the hydrogen bomb as well, would have been revealed as far back as May 1934, which would have given Hitler more than five years in which to develop these ultimate weapons.

The fact that Fermi, and the host of brilliant nuclear physicists and chemists throughout the world, failed to recognize the nature and significance of the world-shaking phenomena they were looking at must go down in history as the Great Five-Year Miracle.

It was the great miracle that saved the world.

In 1925 Ida Noddack had collaborated with her husband in the discovery of the element rhenium. In the paper she published in 1934 she suggested the possibility that Fermi had actually split the uranium atom.

> One may equally well accept [she speculated] that in this new type of nuclear disintegration brought about by neutrons, important nuclear reactions take place other than those hitherto observed. . . . It is conceivable that in the bombardment of heavy nuclei [such as uranium] with neutrons, these nuclei break up into several large fragments which are actually isotopes [twins] of known elements, but are not neighbors of the irradiated elements.

She was, of course, absolutely right, as was learned five years later in a roundabout way after scores of false clues had been followed. But no one considered her suggestion worth even the slightest consideration.

Here we have one of the great paradoxes of history. All human progress is the result of the open mind searching the unknown. Yet here we have a most dramatic illustration of the tightly closed, prejudiced mind saving civilization. Does that mean that the closed mind may sometimes be desirable to serve as a brake against too rapid progress? That we should deliberately slow down the pace of advance of our knowledge of nature to prevent its misuse by brutes and madmen in power? That we should tame the creative mind?

Most certainly not. The events of 1934 prove just the opposite. Instead of the creative mind slowing down, the leaders of civilized nations should recognize the need to speed up their pace to keep in step with the rapid, breath-taking advances of science.

Had that been the case in 1934, there would have been no danger of Hitler being the first possessor of nuclear weapons. On the contrary, had the discovery of nuclear fission been recognized in 1934, when Fermi first split the uranium atom, and had the political and military leaders recognized the vast potentialities of the discovery, the free world, with its much greater industrial and scientific resources would have been the first to produce nuclear weapons. Under such circumstances Hitler, faced with the possibility of nuclear devastation, might well have been deterred from launching the war.

It was only because the political and military leaders of the free world would most certainly have failed to recognize the danger of an atomic arsenal in the hands of Hitler, just as they had failed to recognize the danger to the free world of the vast conventional German war machine, that the failure of the world's top scientists to keep an open mind became a distinct advantage. For the open mind can become a danger only when it functions in a social and political climate of tightly closed minds.

When one contemplates the events from 1934 to the end of 1938, one can only surmise that a benevolent destiny stood watch over the free world and protected it against the forces of evil. It kept the atomic bomb away from the free world's archenemy by blinding the keenest eyes of mankind.

"How come you missed it?" I asked Fermi in 1945, in his laboratory at Los Alamos, New Mexico.

And as he replied I realized for the first time the full extent of the miracle that kept the atomic bomb from Hitler —and gave us a four-year lead over the Soviet Union.

"It was a thin piece of aluminum foil, three mils [thousandths of an inch] thick, that stopped us all from seeing what actually took place," was his answer.

The reason for the aluminum foil was logical enough. Fermi, and the other atomic explorers who repeated his experiment, believed that they were creating new elements out of the uranium in their chamber, elements heavier than uranium. Such transuranium elements, they had calculated, would give off powerful radiations of a certain range. The thin strip of aluminum foil was to serve as a "radiation sieve," holding back the short-range radiations from the uranium but allowing the long-range radiations from the new elements to pass through.

But the three-mil aluminum foil was thick enough to stop Fermi from seeing an altogether new dimension of radiation energy, so great that only the splitting of the uranium atom could have accounted for its appearance.

Had it not been for the shield of three mils of aluminum foil, Fermi would have seen those radiations on the television screen connected to his apparatus, manifesting themselves in the form of jagged high peaks on a vibrating green line. From the height of these peaks, serving as an atomic thermometer, he would have recognized that the energy of the radiations was greater by far than the energy of any radiation ever before observed.

The unprecedented height of the green peaks on the atomic thermometer would have told Fermi that a great cosmic eruption was taking place in his uranium chamber. The height of the jagged peaks on the green line of his television screen would have revealed to him the vast amount of energy carried by these radiations—something on the order of 200 million electron volts.

This astonishing eruption of an atomic volcano could have led to only one conclusion: The splitting of the uranium atom was taking place.

Thus it came to pass that a tiny strip of aluminum foil, three thousandths of an inch thick, interposed itself between the flying fragments of the split uranium atoms and the television screen, hiding from the eyes of man the awesome vision of nuclear power.

Years later I asked Fermi if he regretted having missed making one of the greatest discoveries of all time.

"I am glad I missed," he answered quietly.

Disaster almost came in 1936 in the laboratory of two Swiss physicists, who, like many others, were trying to clear up some of the strange phenomena that were being observed when Fermi's original experiment with uranium was repeated.

One day they forgot to place the three mils of aluminum foil in their uranium chamber. And as they turned their gaze on the television screen they were dazzled by jagged green peaks rising to unbelievable heights. They looked, and the more they looked the more incredible it all seemed to be.

"The damned instrument is sparking," they agreed.

So they discarded their "faulty instrument" and proceeded to set up the experiment with another one of "normal" behavior. This time, and ever after, they remembered to place the three mils of aluminum foil in the proper place inside their chamber.

II. SCIENCE and the World Around Us

II. Science and the World Around Us

An early step in a discussion of "Science and the World around Us" is obviously an examination of the word "world." Used in its narrowest sense of immediate environment, our world has of course been profoundly affected by science. If we consider it in terms of a "cosmos," the changes have been even greater. For the Greeks, the stars were relatively unimportant objects, and the gods dwelt on Mount Olympus. For us the earth is merely a speck in a system that in turn is a speck in unimaginably larger systems; and man has been downgraded accordingly. He can no longer state, "I am monarch of all I survey."

In "The Fourth Adjustment," Harlow Shapley examines the major steps by which this change in perspective has taken place; as well as possible future steps which may occur as our knowledge grows. Shapley was born in Missouri in 1885 and, after working as an astronomer at the Mount Wilson Observatory, became Director of the Harvard College Observatory in 1921. He is well known for his work in photometry and cosmogony and was a pioneer in the use of cepheid variables for the measurement of the distances of globular clusters. He has played a major role in the last of the "four adjustments" he describes by helping to remove the solar system from its long-held position near the center of the Milky Way to its outer regions. He is also the author of such well-known books as Of Stars and Men, from which this selection is taken.

THE FOURTH ADJUSTMENT

HARLOW SHAPLEY

IN THE PAST HISTORY of the evolving human mind, with its increasing knowledge of the surrounding world, there must have been a time when the philosophers of the early tribes began to realize the world is not simply anthropocentric, centered on man himself. As society developed, the village attained central significance—a natural view supported by the evidence of a circular horizon and by the increasing vagueness of the world as one increased the distance from home. But the higher civilizations of the Near and Middle East (and perhaps elsewhere) became increasingly conscious, a few thousand years ago, of the daily revolving sun, stars, and wandering planets. The navigators detected evidence of the curvature of the surface of the oceans and of the earth. The sphericity indicated thereby led to the belief that the center of the earth rather than a surface locality was the center of the visible universe. This view was considered to be consistent with the apparent motions of moon, planets, sun, and stars. The *geocentric* concept thus became the common doctrine in many of the most civilized nations.

This first adjustment of man to the rest of the total material universe was only mildly disturbing to his ego, for man appeared, on pretty good evidence, to surpass all other living forms. He saw little reason to be humble. He personally was not central, but his earth had that distinction.

From Geocentric to Heliocentric

The second adjustment was the abandonment of this earth-center theory. The new hypothesis was not generally acceptable in the Western world until the Copernican Revolution of the sixteenth century soundly established the heliocentric concept. The liberal philosophers and eventually the church fathers yielded to the scientists' theory of a universe centered on our sun. It was a slow shift, for man is a stubborn adherent to official dogma. In time, however, he accepted the sun as the center not only of the local family of planets but also of the total sidereal assemblage; and he long held that view. But it, too, was a fallacy. Another shift was in the making as soon as the sun was recognized as an ordinary star; but only when modern telescopes reported on globular star clusters, galaxies, and cepheid variables did a further adjustment become imperative.

The earth-centered cosmology had been given up in favor of the sun-centered system very reluctantly. And likewise, later, in spite of increasing evidence requiring a further change, the scientists, philosophers, and laymen held doggedly to the heliocentric view. Was this holding fast because of vanity—because of the feeling, cultivated by the unscientific dogmatists, that man is of paramount significance in the world of stars and space-time?

From Heliocentric to Sagittarius and Beyond

There are several better reasons for this second erroneous concept—the heliocentric theory; they are quasi-scientific explanations. For example, the Milky Way follows a great circle; it is a band of light that divides the sky into two practically equal parts. Also, it is of about the same brightness in all parts. By implication, therefore, the sun and earth are centrally located. A second evidence is that the numbers of stars seemed to the early census-takers to fall off with distance from the sun as though it were central; and such a position for his star among the stellar millions brought to man a dignity of position not at all disagreeable. But again it was an illusion.

As late as 1917 the leaders in astronomical interpretation held that the sun was central, or at least very near the center of the sidereal universe. (The galaxies were then not recognized officially as other great stellar systems.) The introduction of the period-luminosity relation for cepheid variable stars as a sounding tool and the determination of the distances and distribution in space of the globular star clusters first indicated the eccentric position of the earth, sun, and surrounding stars in the flattened stellar system which is made manifest by the star-crowded Milky Way.

Gradually came other evidence that the billion-starred nucleus of our spiral galaxy is remotely distant through the southern constellations of Sagittarius, Ophiuchus, and Scorpio. With that thrust into the stellar depths, the heliocentric theory of the stellar universe struggled briefly, weakened, and died.

The center of the galaxy is not near at hand among the bright stars that define those southern constellations, for they are but a few hundred light years away. The center of our galaxy, we have found, is more than twenty-five thousand light years distant. The billions of stars in that nucleus together make the large white glow in the southern Milky Way which we call the Sagittarius star cloud.

The shift from the geocentric to the heliocentric concept doubtless had some philosophical impact in the sixteenth century, but not much. After all, the hot, turbulent, gaseous sun is no place for the delicate array of biological forms in which man finds himself at or near the top. Earth-center or sun-center seemed to make little difference to cosmic thinking. From the deathbed of Copernicus to the birth of this century and later the prevailing heliocentric concept of the stellar universe incited little if any philosophical uneasiness.

But then, with the rapidly increasing accumulation of astronomical information, came the inescapable need for this third adjustment—one that should have deeply affected and to some extent has disturbed man's concern about his place, his career, and his cosmic importance.

This shift of the sun and earth to the edge of our galaxy has considerably eroded human pride and self-assurance; it has carried with it the revelation of the appalling number of comparable galaxies. We could accept rather cheerfully the Darwinian evidence and argument of our animal origin (although the theologians of a century ago found it strong medicine), for that evidence still left us, we believed, at the summit of all terrestrial organisms. But the abandonment of the heliocentric universe, on the basis of dependable astronomical evidence, was certainly deflationary from the standpoint of man's position in the material world, however flattering such advances of human knowledge were to the human mind.

The galactocentric hypothesis puts the earth and its life on the outer fringe of one galaxy in a universe of millions of galaxies. Man becomes peripheral among the billions of stars of his own Milky Way; and according to the revelations of paleontology and geochemistry he is also exposed as a recent, and perhaps an ephemeral manifestation in the unrolling of cosmic time.

At this point we pause for a somber or happy thought, one that is somber or happy depending on one's mood. With the advance of science, and with the retreat of superstition and of belief in the supernatural, we have in recent centuries gone so far and so firmly in our orientation of man in the universe that there is now no retreat! The inquiring human has passed the point of no return. We cannot restore geocentrism or even heliocentrism.

The apes, eagles, and honey bees, with their specialized skills and wisdoms, may be wholly content to be only peripheral ephemerals, and thus miss the great vision that opens before us. For them egocentrism or lococentrism may suffice; for us, no! And since we cannot (and will not) go back to the cramped but comfortable past without sacrificing completely our cultures and civilizations, we go forward; and then we find that there is another chapter in the story of orientation.

Biological Orientation

Another shift must be made, for we are concerned in this discussion not only with the location of our earth in the time and space of the physical world, but with our own location in the biological world. The downgrading of the earth and sun and the elevation of the galaxies is not the end of this progress of scientific pilgrims plodding through philosophic fields. As intimated on previous pages, the need for the further jolting adjustment that now arises above the mental horizon is neither wholly unexpected by workers in scientific fields, nor wholly the result of one or two scientific discoveries. It is a product of the age. We turn from astronomy to the overlap of a dozen other sciences and ask about the spread of life throughout the universe.

As unsolicited spokesmen for all the earthly organisms of

land, sea, and air, again we ask the piquant question: "In this universe of stars, space, and time, *are we alone?*"

From among the many thoughts and measures that promote this Fourth Adjustment of Homo sapiens in the galaxy of galaxies, three phenomena stand out as most meriting our further consideration. The first refers to the number of stars, the second to the catastrophes of ancient days, and the third to the origin of self-replicating molecules. They are worth brief summarizing at this point.

To the ancients only a few thousand stars were known; to the early telescopes, however, a million; and that astounding number has increased spectacularly with every telescopic advance. Finally, with the discovery that the so-called extragalactic nebulae are in reality galaxies, each with its hundreds or even thousands of millions of stars, and with the inability to "touch metagalactic bottom" with the greatest telescopes, we are led to accept the existence of more than 10^{20} stars in our explorable universe, perhaps many more.

The significance of this discovery, or rather of this uncovering, is that we have at hand—that is, the universe has at hand—more than one hundred million million million sources of light and warmth for whatever planets accompany these radiant stars.

(The number of stars and their ages are of course not humanly comprehensible in the usual terms—too many stars, too much space, too many years for minds that are accustomed to operate in serially countable numbers. The macrocosmos transcends our counting. And comprehension is not simplified when we turn to the atomic *micro*cosmos and point out that in our next breath we shall each inhale more than a thousand million million million atoms [10^{21}] of oxygen, nitrogen, and argon.)

The second phenomenon, the expanding Metagalaxy, bears on the question: Do planets accompany at least some of the stars that radiate energy suitable for the complex biological activity that we call life?

We now accept the strong observational evidence of a universal redward shift in the light received from distant external galaxies, and accept also the interpretation of that red-shift as a result of the systematic scattering and diffusion of galaxies and the expansion of the universe. The speed of the mutual recessions is about thirty-five miles a second for galaxies separated by a million light years; twice as fast for galaxies at twice the distance apart; three times at thrice the distance, and so on. The exact numerical values are still under investigation, as is the possible failure to maintain at great separations this uniform increase of scattering speed with distance.

The Turbulence of Long Ago

The rapid dissipation of the Metagalaxy in all directions naturally turns thought to the situation of a year ago when the galaxies were closer together, and to a century, a millennium, a billion years ago. There was of course, as we go back in time, an increasingly greater concentration of the new spreading cosmic units (galaxies). The average density of matter in space at present is very low—something like 10^{-30} grams per cubic centimeter, which on terrestrial standards is a veritable super-super vacuum. A few thousand million years ago, however, the average density in the unexpanded universe must have been so great that collisions of stars and gravitational disruptions of both planets and stars were inevitably frequent.

Now here is an important coincidence. The crust of the earth, radioactively measured, is also a few thousand million years old. Therefore the earth and the other planets of this planetary system were born in those crowded days of turbulence and disastrous encounters.

At that time countless millions of other planetary systems must have developed, for our sun is of a very common stellar type. And stars of nonsolar types must have also participated in the cosmic turmoil. (Our sun, a primitive compared with many blue and red giant stars of recent origin, is so common that in Miss Cannon's famous spectrum catalogue we find some forty thousand sunlike stars, all in our immediate neighborhood.)

Other ways in which planets may be formed, other than this slam-bang process of the early days, have been proposed by astronomers and other scientists. For example, the contraction of protostars out of the hypothecated primeval gas, giving birth to protoplanets on the way, is an evolutionary process now widely favored. It would imply the existence of countless planets.

The head-on collision theory of planetary origin also has been favorably considered in various versions. But the stars are now so widely dispersed that collisions must be exceedingly rare—so very unlikely, in fact, that we might claim uniqueness throughout all creation for ourselves, if planet birth depended only on such collisional procedure. But that vanity cannot be easily maintained, since the expanding universe discovery has shown the crowded, collision-filled conditions when our earth emerged out of the chaos.

Passing over details, we again state the relevant conclusion: *Millions of planetary systems must exist,* and billions is the better word. Whatever the methods of origin, and doubtless more than one type of genesis has operated, planets may be the common heritage of all stars except those so situated that planetary materials would be swallowed up by greater masses or cast off through gravitational action. In passing, we recall that astrophysics has shown that our kind of chemistry and physics prevails throughout the explorable universe. There is nothing uncommon and special here or now.

Remembering our 10^{20} stars and the high probability of millions of planets with suitable chemistry, dimensions, and distance from their nutrient stars, we are ready for the question: On some of these planets is there actually life? Or is that biochemical operation strangely limited to our planet, limited to No. 3 in the family of the sun, which is an average star located in the outer part of a galaxy that contains a hundred thousand million other stars—and this local galaxy but one of millions of galaxies already on the records?

Is life thus restricted? Of course not. We are not alone. And we can accept life's wide dispersion still more confidently when our third phenomenon is indicated.

Biochemistry and microbiology, with the assistance of geophysics, astronomy, and other sciences, have gone so far in bridging the gap between the inanimate and the living that we can no longer doubt but that whenever the physics, chemistry, and climates are right on a planet's surface, life will emerge, persist, and evolve. The mystery of life is vanishing. Objective science is replacing the subjective miraculous. The many researches of the past few years in the field of macromolecules and microorganisms have now made it quite unnecessary to postulate miracles and the supernatural for the origin of life.

The step in human orientation that I call the Fourth Adjustment is ready for the taking, if we care to accept that opportunity. The scattering of galaxies, the abundance of stars, and the structure and habits of macromolecules on warm, moist, star-lit planetary surfaces have prompted this further and most important adjustment in the understanding of the place and functioning of life in the universe. The acceptance of the evidence and the belief that the biological development on this planet is not unique and that varied and highly elaborated sentient life is abundant and widely distributed, have led to the most important step of all in the orientation of Homo in the material world.

Have we come now to the end of the journey, or are there other steps ahead? In view of the rapid growth of scientific techniques and the continual exercise of the logical imagination, it would not be wise to suggest that we shall never *never* find need for further adjustment of the concept of man's place in the universe—that we shall never discover a reason for an orienting adjustment that transcends both the physical and biological orientations, which are now represented respectively by the third and fourth adjustments.

A fifth adjustment might be in the psychological realm, or in the "negative matter" world, or in one of those fanciful existences where our Metagalaxy is only an atom in some super-universe, or in the equally droll (and equally possible) existence where our electrons are the galaxies in some microcosmic universe that is below our measures and our knowing.

In any thorough discussion of science, intangibles must loom large. High school surveys indicate that the average student finds in science none of the glamor of the theater, of sports, or even of business competition. Yet in understanding science there is an excitement more intense than in climbing a mountain; beneath nature's surface beauties there is a deeper beauty, whose contemplation offers the most profound satisfactions.

Aside from the mere discovery of fact, what are these qualities of wonder and pleasure which make the life of science so attractive? Why did W. B. Cannon, to whom we have previously referred, remark that he could not quite understand why he was being paid for doing work he found so enjoyable? Why does Albert Szent-Gyorgyi, a Nobel Laureate in medicine, write that he finds himself running, impatiently, to his laboratory every morning at an early hour? As Director of the Sheffield Scientific School and Dean of the Graduate School at Yale, it has been Dr. Sinnott's function to imbue his students with attitudes such as these. We see how thoroughly he shares them in his description of the ways in which science differs from other disciplines and how through trial and error it grows constantly more worthy of respect. This is a statement not of the necessity but of the sheer admirableness of science and of the pleasure inherent in its pursuit.

SCIENCE AND THE EDUCATION OF FREE MEN

EDMUND W. SINNOTT

TO LEARN THE BASIC FACTS about the universe and its inhabitants, to grow familiar with the laws of matter, energy and living things—surely these are worthy goals indeed. Nowhere can the student come so intimately to grips with the world around him as in the laboratory. Here it is not only with his mind he learns but through his fingers and with all his senses. And what he learns here is of great usefulness, for in our society, so rooted in science and technology, one hardly can become a good citizen who does not know enough of physics and chemistry and biology to understand their practical applications in everyday affairs. Beyond all this, the rigorous disciplines of science develop qualities of utmost value in minds exposed to them. Keen observation, accuracy in report, imagination and sound reasoning are among its products. The sciences have long been so pre-eminent for these great gifts that I need not stress them more. But other and less obvious gifts should concern us, too; fruits of the spirit of science, to be won by those who learn the essence of her doctrine. Four great gifts which science offers to the education of free men I wish to celebrate.

Not least among these is a happy quality of all emancipated minds—the sense of adventure. Those ages when man's spirit has soared have always been times of exploration, of launchings out into the deep, of pushing beyond old horizons into the unknown. They have been eras of excitement over new lands, new ideas, when the vista of man's future widened and the world became a more expansive place.

One fortunate quality of the spirit of science is that it helps to nourish this sense of adventure in a world too inclined to grow static and monotonous. Since the days of the Preacher many have declared that there is no new thing under the sun, that the golden days are behind us, and that ultimate truth has once and for all been given to mankind. We may know little more about the stars than did the Athenians, or about many fundamental questions in logic and the philosophies, but it is certain that of chemistry and physics and biology we understand far more than Aristotle ever did and each year carries us still further on. For science the arrow of time points always forward, never back. One is at liberty to question, if he will, the final value of this progress for mankind, but progress itself no doubter can deny. Here, surely it cannot be illusion. This steady pushing out into the unknown, this never-ceasing conquest of new truth as years go by, gives to the atmosphere of the laboratory a different quality from that which sometimes fills the chambers of the ivory tower. To men of science truth is not a venerated body

of doctrine the great principles of which were long ago discovered by wiser men than we, who can only elaborate upon
them. It is instead a growing, animated thing, warm as with
life and often taking unexpected ways; not to be bound
(however handsomely) in any hundred books, but written
rather in that great volume of the universe so many characters of which man yet must learn.

It is this awareness of a vast body of truth, still undiscovered but discoverable by those who have the skill to
search for it, which gives to science this spirit of adventure,
this sense of great new things to come. Imagine, if you can,
the storm of excitement which forced Kepler to lay down his
pen with trembling fingers when calculation showed that
the heavenly bodies followed laws his genius had foreseen;
or that which must have surged through Darwin's heart
when he read Malthus' essay and found there at last the
clue to Natural Selection. In our own land, what an adventure was that awaiting Morgan in the small laboratory at
Columbia where he bred unpretentious generations of Dro-
sophila, when first he demonstrated the significant relation
between heredity and the behavior of the chromosomes from
which has come the whole magnificent conception of the
physical basis of inheritance. Today in many a laboratory
there is a tingling of suppressed excitement over the im-
minence of other great discoveries by which the frontiers of
expanding knowledge shall be spread wider still. These, too,
are spacious days. No more do barques put out from Bristol
for unknown islands in the Spanish Main, but the adventurers for science still keep alive the spirit of the men who
sailed in them. In a day when many mourn the passing of
the last frontier and the brave days of old, when whispers
are abroad that our society is static, that our civilization has
become "mature," that we have reached a long plateau beyond which nothing new or unforseen may lie—in such a
day science can do for man no greater service than to combat this shameful decadence and to show him how vast are
the regions yet to be explored, how rich the treasures are
which there await the voyager who will set out to gain
them. If ever learning grows perfunctory or stale, the ad-

venturous spirit of the sciences can give it back the vision of a limitless, still undiscovered world.

But what is called the "scientific attitude" has quite another aspect, of equal service for the life of man. The voyagers of science who thus set forth into uncharted seas do not go out as mere adventurers seeking excitement in new horizons, but as merchants of knowledge, hard headed and practical, who are saved from extravagance and romantic futility by the blessing of a critical mind. Whatever treasures they may carry home must undergo dispassionate appraisal and pass every test which doubters can devise. No fact, however exciting, may be accepted by them without close scrutiny of its credentials, nor any hypothesis, whatever its attractiveness, which fails of full support from observation and experiment. Scientists have learned to be wary of obvious facts and plausible ideas. They take to heart the warning of Francis Bacon, that logic alone is no safe guide to truth. How obvious it seemed that a heavier body must fall faster than a lighter one, till Galileo put it to the test; how evident that the apparent speed of light must be affected by the speed of the observer, till the experiment of Michelson and Morley showed this conclusion to be wholly wrong. The universe is full of such traps for the uncritical.

But not by nature is the man of science more critical or careful than his colleagues are. What gives him an advantage over them is that when issues rise in his domain they can be settled with a sureness and dispatch which elsewhere are unknown; for science has a priceless touchstone here to seek out truth—the technique of measurement. Science, so far as it is truly such, must be at bottom quantitative and its material tested and compared by an impersonal measuring stick. Beauty cannot be measured so, nor many other things which men desire. Whether an Epstein sculpture is a thing of beauty or a bore forever may be debated endlessly, but whether the apparent position of a star is altered as light from it passes close to the sun's disk—a question of great moment for Einstein's theory—awaited for its answer only a favorable eclipse and careful measurements. The court of last resort in such a case is always ready, its judgments are decisive and rarely have they been reversed. It is this fortunate fact which lets the scientist move with so sure a step through the mazes of uncertainty into the light of truth. With him are no vague arguments about it and about, no interminable controversies over good or bad, beautiful or ugly, right or wrong; no echoes of those endless conflicts which have agitated men so long. To the clear eye of science these issues often have an air of unreality, like battles between phantoms in the mist. No greater contrast meets the mind than to pass over from the purlieus of the ivory tower, with its soft shadows, its pastels and greys, its homage to the great imponderables of sense and spirit, and to enter the bright light of the laboratory, where all seems white or black, all true or false, cleansed of uncertainty and the germs of doubt and trusting to the intellect alone. Here is a different climate altogether. The scientist is not unmindful of those high uncertainties which so engage his colleagues, nor does he doubt their grave significance. What sets apart from theirs the world in which he lives is that it deals instead with tough, concrete and measurable things which answer, if accosted properly, with unequivocating yea or nay. This great advantage the scientist must prize above all else, and not to press it home relentlessly would be to him the one sin unforgivable. His critical, skeptical attitude is thus by no means one of bilious suspicion and distrust, but simply a persistent attempt to subject every statement, every idea, every theory to the pitiless criterion of objective test, to hold against it some measuring stick of strict appraisal by which alone it then must stand or fall. Thus only can the scientist save his work from the perils of obscurity and dogma. Thus only can he plant his feet on a secure foundation in the universe.

This attitude of critical-mindedness is one of the chief gifts which understanding of the sciences bestows, a major contribution which it can make to the education of free men. In an age like ours, when men are carried about by every wind of doctrine, when propaganda is the mightiest of weapons and the councils of freedom are beclouded by complexity of issues, confusion and deliberate falsehood, hope for a rational society of man lies in the cultivation of that clear and critical mind by which alone truth can be separated from error.

The adventurous spirit and the critical mind—these are two qualities which mark the man of science as he cultivates his corner of the field of human knowledge. And from his labor two great harvests grow, not lacking in the other corners of the field but thriving with luxuriance in the rich soil of the scientific spirit.

First among these is freedom. When one sets out upon the serious and difficult business of wresting from the universe more knowledge of its character and qualities, his efforts must all meet with failure unless he can move with perfect freedom toward the truth wherever the path may lead. No authority must stay him there; no tradition perplex him; no dogma, no prejudice, no vested interest prevent the thorough exploration of every promising avenue he sees. From its beginning, science has struggled to be free from all such man-made bondage. Sometimes its chief battles have been against external coercion of a church or king or state, or such sinister forces as those which now attempt to put the mind in chains. Oftener the bonds are more insidious—temptations to conform to prejudice or tradition or desire, to follow still the old accustomed road when a new highway proves a better one and thus demands diversion to its course of the mind's traffic. Repeatedly science has proved her freedom here to follow truth with but a single purpose. One thinks of how Darwin's theory, though running counter to the beliefs of laymen and of scientists alike, convinced biologists that evolution was a fact and thus compelled them to revise completely their ideas not only as to the origin and relationships of living things but as to the very character of life itself. So, too, we can remember how physics in a generation past was shaken by the discovery of radioactivity and by other new ideas and how it scrapped old ideologies and cheerfully set its steps in unfamiliar ways. Textbooks were thrown away. Ancient ideas long held as axiomatic were abandoned. These were no occasions for regret but rather for rejoicing, since from new knowledge came a keener insight into the nature of the universe and man.

Science thus breathes the very air of freedom, and offers in a day of peril and confusion a mighty reinforcement to the free spirit of man. By bitter trial we have learned at last that this free spirit is no natural gift but must be nourished and defended or it will be lost.

"But," you may ask, "in this confusion and catastrophe why single out the scientist as freedom's champion? Are there not others at the barricades who fight as well as he?" Surely there are, and happily many such. Science is but one of all those precious things which perish when authority and force succeed in fettering the spirit of man. To fight such manifest tyranny many swords are drawn. But it is against those subtler forces of oppression—against provincialism, prejudice, intolerance and all their kind—that science leads the battle.

For science can never be provincial. A discovery in physics coming from Germany is welcomed to the treasury of knowledge as readily as if from England. A Russian biologist collaborates fruitfully with American colleagues who work in the same field. These men all speak the same great language of ideas. Indeed the international congresses of the sciences, more than the ill-starred gatherings by Lake Geneva, were truly parliaments of man and proved that national barriers need not prevent harmonious coöperation on a global scale.

Science cannot be prejudiced. What color a man's skin may be or what his politics or social class—differences which arouse antagonisms so violent that they are surely a chief peril for mankind today—these have no standing in the laboratory. Einstein, the Duc de Broglie and George Washington Carver here meet as equals and are judged alone by contributions which they make to scientific knowledge. Preposterous ideas of "Aryan" physics or "Jewish" mathematics or "bourgeois" astronomy all have met with the derision they deserved.

And above all science can never be intolerant. Those fundamental divergencies in ideals, beliefs and faiths which through all history have broken up the human family hold no meaning for her. She knows no party line, no sect, no orthodoxy. She judges ideas solely for themselves and never asks what company they keep.

To free men's minds from all these forms of bondage is our great concern, and in this task, to which all liberal studies are dedicated, the great example of the sciences stands as a brilliant beacon which will light the way. Science and freedom are inseparable.

But freedom is not all. Another harvest from the field which science cultivates, as necessary to mankind as liberty itself, is faith. This claim may seem to many a surprising, even a preposterous, one; for men of science too rarely have been known as men of faith. But in a truer sense they really are, for understanding of the sciences and of the laws with which they deal confers a deep and fundamental confidence in the very nature of the universe itself which is the necessary basis of all other faith.

In her pursuit of truth science passes through freedom to certainty. The liberty she prizes is not a goal, an end within itself, but a means only. It is essential in reconnaissance, in those wide explorations which precede discovery. For voyagers here the freedom of the seas must be complete. Once the discovery is made, however, and the voyage is done, then freedom has no longer any meaning. When a new fact or principle has been established by careful search and critical appraisal, as when from a swarm of hypotheses one ultimately survives all tests and is raised finally to be a law, then tolerance for a diversity of incompatible ideas about it, so necessary in the earlier stages of the pursuit of truth, quite loses its significance. Tolerance of proven error would be monstrous. Thus two hundred years ago the nature of combustion was still obscure, and many theories were explored to account for this remarkable process; but the discovery of oxidation by Lavoisier cleared up the matter. No chemist now preserves an open mind on the phlogiston theory. He is not intolerant. He simply ignores what once was possible truth but now is known for error. Physics today is undecided as to whether light should be regarded as a series of waves or a series of particles. There is evidence for each view, and the minds of physicists are freely open; but if one of these theories should be definitely established as the true one, such open-mindedness would vanish overnight.

Thus science slowly builds her edifice, incorporating in it, one by one, those facts and principles established by rigorous testing and the trial of time. This splendid fabric has grown steadily through the years, the triumph of man's intellect, the visible body of truth which he has sifted from a mass of error. Here is no dim mirage but an island of certainty rising from the great sea of doubt; something dependable and sure to which the mind may anchor confidently. These findings of the scientist may not be "truer" in the ultimate sense than others of a sponsorship much less austere. In the wide realm of values they may often seem of little worth. Truth is an elusive goal, at best, but if anything in this precarious world is made of the very stuff of certainty, it is these. If firm foundation for belief lies anywhere, it is here.

Such increased knowledge, piling fact on fact and formulating laws which can interpret them, all this will help a man to look at nature with assurance, as one who is already in her confidence, and will relieve him of that incubus of fear and mystery by which the unenlightened are oppressed. But from the material world thus seen so clearly and thus known so well there comes the evidence of things not seen, the basis of a confidence in something deeper still, the essence of a faith. For what confers upon these facts their high significance is that behind them stands the tremendous assurance of dependability in the universe itself. The whole experience of science from the beginning speaks here with single voice. Nature is never capricious, never inconstant. To the same question she will always give the same reply. Perform an experiment today and it will give the result that it did yesterday and will again tomorrow, if all conditions are identical. This great generalization presents the magnificent picture of an orderly, constant and dependable universe, no longer strange and unpredictable. It is the one secure foundation upon which any science can be built, or any rational world.

From this basic faith may be extrapolated philosophies of the most varied kind. Some men have drawn from it a sure conclusion that the universe is rigidly determined, a system closed and certain, where freedom is illusion and the urgencies of choice and passion and desiring are unrealistic and meaningless. To others such a philosophy seems far too circumscribed and pallid. They postulate a less naive determinism in those complex protoplasmic systems which we are, and look for reservations broad enough to give the human spirit latitude. Wherever in this ancient controversy our sympathies may lie, we all agree in seeking among these higher provinces of human life, which still are so obscure, an assurance of order and of faithfulness like that so evident in the simpler realm of science. Surely the universe must at last be one.

Scientists have often been denounced as faithless men, and indeed they have shattered many an ancient belief, outgrown and serviceable no longer; but far more important than this is the great service of the disciplines of science in justifying to man the possibility—nay, the necessity—of profound conviction, of sure certainty. For freedom by itself lacks motive power. The zealot, the believer, the man aflame with a great faith, is he who leads the crusades and propagates the gospels. The drive and enthusiasm which bring great things to pass belong to those who are convinced, not those who are uncertain. We are apt to undervalue a fundamental trait in man—his desperate craving for certainty. The certainties of science provide just this conviction and furnish an indispensable foundation for the faiths of men.

But here one may object again that man's beliefs and his convictions have been nourished more by emotion than by intellect and that men of science will hardly write great hymns of faith or lead forlorn hopes in defense of an abstraction. It is surely true that these much warmer faiths which for so long have comforted mankind will still inspire him and will lead him on; yet the conviction of the scientist, which burns with cooler flame, may well endure when others have grown weak. It is the pilot light of faith, steadily burning with little sound or heat, but needed to enkindle greater fires. To light this small flame in the souls of men is a great service of the sciences.

Such are among the offerings which science brings to the great task of educating free men for a free world. They are not gifts for which men know her best. She oftener stands for services of quite another sort—for the perfection of marvelous machines, for that increased control of energy which makes mankind the master of his world, and for developing those skills by which he gains food and can fight disease. These are great gifts, indeed. But science at our hands deserves a higher place than merely as a gadgeteer for man, giving him tools and the command of them, or even as a teacher of precision and sound reasoning. To everyone who comes to know her well she gives both forward look and critical appraisal, both the adventurous spirit and the cautious mind. And more perhaps than any other field of knowledge science unites a free and tolerant spirit with that conviction and sure certainty which furnish the motive power to drive it on. There are many truths, indeed, which science cannot teach, whole realms of wisdom and experience to which she holds no key, but the resources in her treasury are immensely richer than most of us imagine. For science is the spirit of our age. Our minds are tingling with its impact. It goes from strength to strength to dominate the lives of men, and has the power to work us infinite good or ill. The mastery it gives of energy and of material things may send our race careening to its doom unless we gain the wisdom and the sanity to control our course.

It has been the ill fate of science and the humanities that they have so often failed to understand each other's aims and essence. In the case of science, this failure has extended to the man in the street, due partly to his ignorance of scientific vo-

cabulary. He is prepared to discuss art, politics, and economics, but he approaches science with blank uneasiness. As C. P. Snow remarks, he has no exact understanding of even such a fundamental scientific concept as acceleration. Yet he would have no great difficulty with such a concept. The basic meaningfulness of science is as easily grasped as those of the arts and humanities. There is a profound parallel between the intellectual and aesthetic satisfactions each has to offer. Science is human in its aims, its methods, and its achievements. Instead of destroying culture, it offers unique insights for its development.

Jacob Bronowski is qualified by his own interests and activities to write of this relationship. By profession he is a mathematician, formerly a Senior Lecturer at University College at Hull. An expert on statistical analysis, he wrote the British report on "The Effects of the Atomic Bomb at Hiroshima and Nagasaki" and is Director General of the Process Development Department of the National Coal Board. His deep interest in the relationship between science and the humanities is revealed in his books The Common Sense of Science and Science and Human Values. He has also written two well-known works of literary criticism, The Poet's Defense and William Blake: A Man without a Mask, and a number of dramatic works, including the prize-winning The Face of Violence, which has been broadcast throughout Europe.

SCIENCE AND SENSIBILITY

JACOB BRONOWSKI

I

I CAME TO ENGLAND when I was twelve, and when I landed I could speak, rather badly, two words of English which I had learnt on the channel boat. I did not read English at all easily for two or three years after. The first writers in whom I was able to distinguish what my patient schoolmasters called style were, I remember, Macaulay and Joseph Conrad. I do not remember now whether at that time I was able to distinguish between their styles. I read greedily, with excitement, with affection, with a perpetual sense of discovering a new and, I slowly realised, a great literature. But I was handicapped then, and I have been ever since, by the disorderly way in which I fell upon my masterpieces: Dickens cheek by jowl with Aphra Behn and Bernard Shaw, and elsewhere leaving tracts of neglected literature by the century. To this day I have not read the Waverley novels, and in consequence I have remained rather insensitive to historical romance, particularly if much of the conversation is in dialect.

I make these confessions because they seem to me to bear on many stories besides my own. The difficulties which I had are not mine alone, and they are not in any special way literary difficulties. On the contrary, what now strikes me about them is their likeness to the trouble which other people have with science. At bottom my difficulties in facing a strange literature are precisely the difficulties which all intelligent people today have in trying to make some order out of modern science.

We live surrounded by the apparatus of science: the Diesel engine and the experiment, the bottle of aspirins and the survey of opinion. We are hardly conscious of them; but behind them we are becoming conscious of a new importance in science. We are coming to understand that science is not a haphazard collection of manufacturing techniques carried out by a race of laboratory dwellers with acid-yellow fingers and steel-rimmed spectacles and no home life. Science, we are growing aware, is a method and a force of its own, which has its own meaning and style and its own sense of excitement. We are aware now that somewhere within the jungle of valves and formulae and shining glassware lies a content; lies, let us admit it, a new culture.

How are we to reach that culture, across its jargons, and translate it into a language which we know? The difficulties of the layman are my boyhood difficulties. He opens his

newspaper and there stands a revelation in capitals: THE
ELECTRONIC BRAIN, OR SUPERSONIC FLIGHT, or *Is there life
on Mars?* But capitals or italics, the revelation remains in
code for him. The language is as strange to him as *The
Anatomy of Melancholy* was to me at fifteen. He has only
the smallest vocabulary: a smattering from other popular
articles, schoolboy memories of the stinks lab, and a few
names of scientists sprinkled at random across history. His
history, which might have given an order to it all, is the
most maddening of his uncertainties. I knew no English history, and therefore I could not make sense of literary development. How well I recall the helplessness with which
I faced a list of names such as Marlowe and Coleridge and
H. G. Wells. I could not make any historical order of them.
It is hard to visualize my difficulty; yet just this is the difficulty which every reader meets when he sees the names of
Napier, Humphry Davy and Rutherford. These three scientists were contemporaries of the three writers, and they were
by no means lesser men.

II

A knowledge of history of course, even the history of
science, will not do duty for science. But it gives us the
backbone in the growth of science, so that the morning
headline suddenly takes its place in the development of our
world. It throws a bridge into science from whatever humanist interest we happen to stand on. And it does so because it asserts the unity not merely of history but of
knowledge. The layman's key to science is its unity with the
arts. He will understand science as a culture when he tries
to trace it in his own culture.

It has been one of the most destructive modern preju-
dices that art and science are different and somehow incompatible interests. We have fallen into the habit of op-
posing the artistic to the scientific temper; we even identify
them with a creative and a critical approach. In a society
like ours which practises the division of labor there are of
course specialised functions, as matters of convenience. As a

convenience, and only as a convenience, the scientific function is different from the artistic. In the same way the function of thought differs from, and complements, the function of feeling. But the human race is not divided into thinkers and feelers, and would not long survive the division.

Much of this quarrel between science and soul was trumped up by the religious apologists of Queen Victoria's day, who were anxious to find science materialistic and unspiritual. The sneer that science is only critical came from others. It was made by the timid and labored artists of the nineties in order that they might by comparison appear to be creative and intuitive. Yet this finesse could not hide their own knowledge that the best minds were already being drawn to the more adventurous practice of the new sciences: a movement which Peacock had foreseen seventy-five years before in *The Four Ages of Poetry*.

The arts and the sciences ever since have been in competition for the mostly lively young brains. This competition is itself the clearest evidence that good minds can fulfil themselves as well in one as in the other. Here in fact is one of the few psychological discoveries of our generation to which we can hold with a reasonable certainty: that the general configuration of intelligence factors which distinguish the bright from the dull is the same in one man as another, in the humanist as in the scientist. We are divided by schooling and experience; and we do differ, though we differ less, in our aptitudes; but below these, we share a deeper basis of common ability. This is why I write with confidence for laymen and scientists, because the reader who is interested in any activity which needs thought and judgment is almost certainly a person to whom science can be made to speak. It is not he who is deaf, but the specialists who have been dumb—the specialists in the arts as well as the sciences.

Many people persuade themselves that they cannot understand mechanical things, or that they have no head for figures. These convictions make them feel enclosed and safe, and of course save them a great deal of trouble. But the reader who has a head for anything at all is pretty sure to have a head for whatever he really wants to put his mind to. His interest, say in mathematics, has usually been killed by routine teaching, exactly as the literary interest of most scientists (and, for that matter, of most non-scientists) has been killed by the set book and the Shakespeare play. Few people would argue that those whose taste for poetry has not survived the School Certificate are fundamentally insensitive to poetry. Yet they cheerfully write off the large intellectual pleasures of science as if they belonged only to minds of a special cast. Science is not a special sense. It is as wide as the literal meaning of its name: knowledge. The notion of the specialised mind is by comparison as modern as the specialised man, "the scientist," a word which is only a hundred years old.

III

Therefore I have in mind, as I write, a reader who is less interested in the sciences than he is in science. There was in the last century a tradition of self-teaching in the Mechanics' Institutes, which in its time was a just cause for pride. But the tradition is gone and its going now is not a loss, because the interest in science has widened. We are all aware of the widening. Those who hanker after a knowledge of science today are not looking for technical information. They are no longer unfortunates who would have liked to work in a laboratory too, if fate had not sent them into a mill at twelve. I take it for granted that those who take up this book are well content with what they know and do, and are not thinking of themselves vicariously as the white-coated hero of a second feature about the discovery of Compound E. And I do not assume that they must necessarily be fascinated by the marvels of the electron microscope or of radioactive iodine. I think of them as people aware that the world into which they were born is changing during their lifetime, and who have about this change the same curiosity which they have about what is new in their closer neighborhood—in literature or the arts or local politics or the business of the tennis club.

Few people today are really in doubt about the scale and

the lasting importance of this change. But many people push it to the back of their minds, resolutely or in embarrassment. And much of the time they fear to face it, because they are afraid to acknowledge that this movement is changing their lives, is washing away the landmarks of their familiar world, rising round their values and in the end drowning the selves which must last them their lifetime. Yet these fears are less fears of the social change which science is working than simple personal fears. They are afraid, we are all afraid of being left out. We are afraid that something is happening which we shall not be able to understand and which will shut us out from the fellowship of the brighter and younger people.

These fears I believe are groundless. I believe that it is easy for a man who likes conversation and to read the second leader now and again to be comfortable with the large ideas of science: as easy as it is for a scientist to have a fancy for biography. The difficulties are those of language and the personal fear of what is unfamiliar. These are merely fed by those enthusiastic scientists who write as if the layman were to be pitied, and treat him as an erring would-be scientist who ought to be converted to an interest in the nucleus. I have no such reader in mind. I think of my readers, scientists as well as laymen, as balanced people who see about them the world in movement, and who want to know enough about the forces of science outside their own neighborhood to assess their part in that profound and total movement of history.

IV

Many people affect to believe that science has progressively strangled the arts, or distorted them into some unpleasant "modern" form; and therefore that the arts can be revived only by throwing over science. Often, of course, this is merely an elderly sentiment in favor of the art of our younger days, and the real scapegoat is not science but change. But even where the sentiment is less partial, it springs from a misunderstanding of progress in art and science. Science today is plainly more powerful than, let us say, in the time of Isaac Newton. Against this, the arts today seldom reach the height of, say, his contemporary John Dryden. It is therefore tempting to conclude that science continually outgrows its older ideas, while great literature remains permanent. But this is a hopeless muddle of concepts. Newtons are no more plentiful today than Drydens; and the work of Newton continues to stand to modern science in precisely the relation that the prose of Dryden stands to modern prose. Dryden and Newton each revealed a wholly new set of possibilities in their forms of knowledge. Both are classics in this sense, that they were at once pioneers and men of great achievement. And neither is a classic in any other sense.

The belief that science destroys culture is sometimes supported by historical statements that the arts have flourished only when the sciences have been neglected. This thesis is so directly contrary to history that I find it difficult to begin to debate it. What is this golden age of art untarnished by the breath of rude mechanics? Where did it exist? In the East? The civilisations of Egypt, of India, and of the Arabs belie it. The only oriental poet at all well known in England, Omar Khayyam, was a Persian astronomer. In the West? The culture of the West begins in Greece; and in the great age of Greece, art and science penetrate one another more closely than in any modern age. Pythagoras lived before Aeschylus had created Greek drama. Socrates taught when that drama was at its greatest; and is Socrates to be claimed by art or science? And Plato, who did not tolerate poets in his ideal state, was a scholar when Aristophanes closed the eyes of Greek drama. The example of these men in science as much as in art set the modern world afire in the Renaissance. And the type and symbol of Renaissance man was from the beginning and remains Leonardo da Vinci, painter, sculptor, mathematician, and engineer. No man has shown more strikingly the universality and the unity of the intellect.

In England we put the golden age into the reign of Queen Elizabeth; and that characteristically was an age of commercial and industrial as well as of literary invention. Voyagers and adventurers like Sir Walter Raleigh were the Leonardos of that age; and Raleigh's own circle, which turned Christopher Marlowe into a rationalist, was dominated by a mathematician and astronomer, Thomas Hariot. For navigation is dependent on astronomy; it went hand in hand with the new speculations about the world and the solar system; and in turn, the voyages of the great navigators inspired the literature of Elizabethan England. The worlds of art and of science and the physical world unfolded then together. It was not by accident that the first table of logarithms was published within a few years of the First Folio.

Sixty years after the death of Elizabeth, another great age ripened in England, the age of Restoration literature. One symbol of the age is the founding of what has remained the most important scientific society in the world. The meeting which founded it, on November 28, 1660, opened with a lecture on astronomy, and the lecture was given by Christopher Wren, the architect. The society was given its name, the Royal Society, and its motto by the most enthusiastic of its founders. He was John Evelyn, the diarist. When the society wanted to encourage the use of simple and lucid prose, it appointed a committee which included a fellow of the society with a special gift for such writing. He was the poet John Dryden.

V

The golden ages of literature were in fact times of greatness when science and the arts went forward hand in hand. Has all this come to an end? Literary critics say, Yes, it.ended in England at the Industrial Revolution, somewhere between 1760 and 1800. Yet these critics date the Romantic Revival from some point between the death of Collins in 1759, which means so much to Wordsworth, and the publication of the *Lyrical Ballads* in 1798. These two sets of dates are almost identical, and can it be reasonable to keep them in separate compartments of the mind? Is it really tenable to think of the Industrial Revolution as a kind of death? It gave our world its structure. It turned science from astronomy to what are essentially its modern interests, which hinge on the use of mechanical power. And it created in the romantic poets and the reformers what has remained our sensibility.

I say created our sensibility, although of course I have pointed only to the coincidence of dates: that Blake and Coleridge and Wilberforce were after all contemporaries of Arkwright and James Watt. Against this, those who hold the illusion that pre-industrial England was more sensitive and cultured, point to the misery of the manufacturing age: women in mines, children in factories, the disasters of enclosure, famine, the Napoleonic wars, and political reaction. These were very terrible evils, but they are evils far older than 1800 and the machines. The labor of women and children for endless hours in their own homes is a commonplace in Defoe's journals in 1725. Yet the Augustan optimists of his day did not see it as matter for protest. But in the factory these evils became naked and public; and the driving force for reform came from the men of the mill, from Robert Owen and the elder Peel. We today are scandalized that boys went on climbing chimneys for nearly eighty years after the heart-rending poems which Blake wrote about them around 1790; the last of the climbing boys, Joseph Lawrence, is still alive as I write. But the boys had been climbing for a hundred years before Blake without a line of protest from Addison or Gay or Dr. Johnson. In their broad Augustan day, Scottish miners were legally still serfs, just as the miners of Greece had always been slaves; and neither civilisation thought anything amiss. So today in China and India and other countries with few machines, life is brutal and laborious, and sensibility is unknown; I have seen it so myself, under the rusty thin surface of mechanization in Japan, for women and animals alike. It was the engine, it was the horsepower which created consideration for the horse; and the Industrial Revolution which created our sensibility.

VI

Science changes our values in two ways. It mjects new ideas
into the familiar culture. And it subjects it to the pressure
of technical change, in the way I have just been describing, until the whole basis of our culture has imperceptibly
been remade. The invention of printing does not seem to
bear very directly on the content of poetry. But when a
poem can be read and read again, it is natural that the interest shifts from the rhythm to the meaning and the allusion.
So the invention of photography has made the painter and
the patron lose interest in the likeness and transfer it to
some more formal pattern. Our whole sensibility has been re-
created by such subtle shifts.

Science and the arts today are not as discordant as many
people think. The difficulties which we all have as intelligent amateurs in following modern literature and music
and painting are not unimportant. They are one sign of the
lack of a broad and general language in our culture. The
difficulties which we have in understanding the basic ideas
of modern science are signs of the same lack. Science and
the arts shared the same language at the Restoration. They
no longer seem to do so today. But the reason is that they
share the same silence: they lack the same language. And it
is the business of each of us to try to remake that one universal language which alone can unite art and science, and
layman and scientist, in a common understanding.

In the year 1940, man's dream of creating a new element, which chemists had pursued since the days of the alchemists, was achieved with the discovery of neptunium and plutonium. In the following year, the fissionable isotope of plutonium, which has played so important a part in the production of atomic energy, was isolated; and other transuranium elements were discovered later.

The name most intimately connected with these researches is that of Glenn T. Seaborg. Born in Michigan in 1912, he studied physics and chemistry at the University of California. He served an apprenticeship under E. O. Lawrence, the Nobel Prize-winning inventor of the cyclotron, and became a member of the faculty, working at the Lawrence Radiation Laboratory. From 1942 to 1946 he was in charge of the chemical separation section of the atomic energy project in Chicago. Returning to California, he became Chancellor of the University in 1958. With E. M. McMillan he was awarded the Nobel prize in chemistry in 1951. In 1961, he was appointed Chairman of the United States Atomic Energy Commission by President Kennedy.

A mere recital of Seaborg's achievements and the honors he has received indicates how closely he has been able to observe both the scientific and the political aspects of the most important problem of our day. As he points out in this article, our society is entering a new era—it has ingested science but has not yet begun to digest and assimilate it. The dilemma is posed by a power that could usher in an age of great plenty or of unimaginable destruction. Here Seaborg discusses the relationship between science on the one hand, and society, humanism, democracy, and freedom on the other. Calm, thoughtful, yet terrifying in its implications, "A Scientific Society—The Beginnings" needs to be pondered carefully. "Each of us," says Seaborg, in this speech to an audience of scientists and engineers, "needs a sense of responsibility and urgency." The advice applies to all of us if the race is to survive.

A SCIENTIFIC SOCIETY—THE BEGINNINGS

GLENN T. SEABORG

JOHN WESLEY POWELL was a man who stands large in the history of American science.[1] He believed in the frontier, and he lived on it vigorously and adventurously, whether exploring the Colorado or insisting upon good science policy in Washington. Powell was a man of great vision. He saw clearly how science and engineering could develop the vast potential of the West to help make ours a great nation. He understood the nature of science and technology, and his Geological Survey demonstrated the usefulness of properly administered government science. It is with pride, therefore, that I speak in Powell's name, here in the West he knew so well.

As I prepared for this lecture and considered some of the developments in science since Powell's time, my thoughts drifted to personal reminiscence. I recalled that in this season 21 years ago, my colleagues and I were doing the experiment which resulted in the discovery of plutonium. Needless to say, my world has not been the same since. Nor has my experience been unusual. The same forces that have operated in my case have markedly altered the lives of many millions of people and, indeed, society itself. Granted that allowance must be made for the lack of perspective that accompanies our closeness to the events, it still seems pardonable to judge the past two decades to be one of the most portentous periods in human history. And this has been the result of science and technology.

I believe these things to be true not alone because of man's novel dilemma, revolving about nuclear weapons and

1. This is the John Wesley Powell lecture, delivered 27 December 1961 at the Denver meeting of the American Association for the Advancement of Science.

the very survival of modern civilization, but also because of the general scientific-technological progress most dramatically exemplified by the peaceful atom and by space exploration.

What is perhaps more important in the long run, granted our ability to avert total nuclear war, is the fact that in these two decades science and technology have become a dominant force in our social order. Much has been written about the scientific society, usually in the future tense. I believe we are warranted in changing the tense to the present. Although it is in its infancy, the scientific society has arrived; it has crossed the threshold in its relationship to society as a whole.

Science and technology are now part of the fabric of government, industry, and business, and of our social institutions. The destinies of individuals and peoples are irrevocably associated, from day to day, with the growth and use of scientific knowledge.

As was to be expected, the birth of the new infant has not been an easy one. Nor will its development be untroubled. It seems clear that science and technology are the most powerful forces for material advancement unleashed by man. The changes these forces bring—and will continue to bring—run wide and deep through society. Men as a whole are not friendly to such changes and forces. But to scientists, these developments may seem clearer than to most men.

The conception of our infant scientific society can best be assigned to the Renaissance. At that time, men challenged authority and the dogma that had ruled for centuries and questioned the nature of the universe and man's place in it. This spirit of questioning in the Western world occurred on many fronts—in religion and philosophy and political theory, in art and literature, and in science. One important result was the expression in the Declaration of Independence and the Bill of Rights of the Constitution of the idea of individual personal, political, and intellectual freedom as controlling in an organized society. The same forces that liberated men politically, and in other ways, also produced the scientific method. With the growth of freedom of inquiry and the development of techniques for discovery, there began an acceleration of our ideas about nature. And the knowledge gained became highly significant when translated by technologists into tools.

Through our privileged perspective, we can see that, given the conditions of the last five centuries, everything that has happened has been virtually inevitable. For the achievement by men of the right to search for truth was the critical breakthrough. When this right was established on a continuing basis, it was only a matter of time until bacteria were discovered, electricity was identified, and nuclear fission was revealed. In a word, modern scientific knowledge and its application are a consequence of the vigorous exercise of the freedoms that arose in Western Europe and America.

I should like to introduce my stocktaking of the 20 years now ending by recalling some personal experiences to illustrate, in an anecdotal way, something of the changes within science and its new relationships to society.

In the fall of 1940 I was a young chemist at the University of California. We had been trained to believe that a deep gulf ran between pure and applied science. I was "pure," of course, searching for knowledge for its own sake. We were also poor—a property which followed purity like the night the day. But being pure, we could accept poverty with good grace and even with some pride. Our poverty, of course, pervaded our research operations. Research funds were almost unknown. We built as much of our equipment as we could, or coaxed our more talented friends into helping with it. Laboratory space was hard to come by. I can recall, as a graduate student, adopting the squatter's-rights technique to obtain some space in an abandoned and condemned old wooden structure. But these were the accepted conditions of research science in those days, and we were hardly aware that our difficulties were difficulties.

The Lawrence Radiation Laboratory was a new kind of

thing on the scientific horizon. It gave us a foretaste of things to come in some fields. The equipment was huge—by 1939 there were two cyclotrons that were giants of scientific instrumentation. Scientists from a variety of fields found it profitable frequently to pool their talents in working with the cyclotrons and their products. In this way many of us encountered the emerging concept of group research. The laboratory budget, mostly from private sources, was considered enormous for the time, although this view might arouse some amusement today.

Of course, we were not unaware of what was happening in the world—of the war that had started, and of the power-mad dictator who was a threat to our ideals and who aspired to engulf humanity in his medieval social order. But, like many research scientists, I did not then relate my work very much to practical things, and certainly not to war.

Until 1940, my research had been concerned with the identification—with J. J. Livingood, primarily—of new radioisotopes. In the spring of that year, Edwin M. McMillan and Phillip H. Abelson opened the transuranium field with their brilliant discovery of element 93, neptunium. It is an interesting commentary on the thinking and the priorities of the time that McMillan, who had started work aimed toward the discovery of the next higher element— element 94—was called away to do defense research on radar at the Massachusetts Institute of Technology.

With the assent of McMillan, three of us—my associate the late Joseph W. Kennedy, Arthur C. Wahl, at that time a graduate student, and I—undertook to continue the research. It seems doubtful that many theses have been written that contained significance to rival that of Wahl's. A few days before Christmas, in 1940—just 21 years ago—the cyclotron bombardment was made which, in the succeeding few weeks, resulted in the, chemical identification of plutonium. Plutonium may be said to have "come of age" as this meeting of the AAAS takes place.

Even at Christmas time in 1940 our work was not done in an atmosphere heavy with a sense of historical import, but rather in the carefree manner of young adventurers breaking new ground. It is true that fission and its implications were then known, and that some steps were being taken to learn how to exploit this discovery, in work with uranium-235. It was theoretically postulated, too, that an isotope of element 94 might be fissionable. Yet there was not, 21 years ago, any clear idea of how the then-identified element, if discovered, could be practically made in quantity and how it could be put to use as a military weapon.

Subsequently, with Emilio Segrè, we created and identified the fissionable isotope plutonium-239, in March 1941. And a way was soon visualized to make this element in quantity and to use it as a weapon. In a short time the knowledge gained in the search for truth became a formidable bulwark of national defense.

We crossed the divide between science and technology, and our work became useful in many ways, including its significant contributions to our arsenal of defense. We went from poverty to relative riches. Instead of working alone or with a colleague or two, we banded together in the team research pattern now so well established.

At times, during the war, we dreamed of a kind of scientific V-day after which we would return to the old ways, most especially the pursuit of knowledge for the sake of knowledge alone and divorced from application. Some of you probably were with me in the great hegira to fundamental research which actually did occur at the end of the war.

However, a large number of us found that the conditions of science had changed, in varying ways and to varying degrees. Perhaps the central point is that two decades ago science was called up, as it had been in the Civil War and in World War I, to fight a five-alarm blaze. But this time, in a sense, science did not return to the firehouse.

The use of the nuclear bomb crystallized, as never before and on a world stage, the enormous power of science and technology. But this power was not to be confined to war alone, but was to be used for man's benefit in the expansion of industrial productivity and the advancement of our economic system generally. Later in the two decades of which I speak, Sputnik further dramatized the lesson.

Moreover, the realization grew among us and among industrial and political leaders that the time fuse between discovery and application had become short and was growing shorter. The gulf between basic and applied science had narrowed, and in some instances had become imperceptible. This realization was expressed in many ways: for example, while the government after World War II continued the development of nuclear weapons, it dared not fail to support, at the same time, the fundamental research in particle physics. In addition, under the conditions of modern competition between great nations, the prestige and power of a society came to be measured in part by its accomplishments in the growth of all knowledge.

In the past two decades, then, science has come to stay, as a regular, essential, and pervasive activity in modern society. The signs that ours has become a scientific society are all around us. Suffice it to say here that government, business, and industry are dependent for survival and expansion not alone on technology but on an accelerating growth of knowledge deriving from research that once was sometimes described as "pure." Moreover, it appears that nearly everyone is aware of this fact.

Let me give you just one example of these developments, relating to the governmental agency of which I have the honor to be chairman. In 1940 there was no such thing as atomic energy. Today, atomic energy is one of our biggest enterprises. The capital investment of the Atomic Energy Commission is $7.5 billion before depreciation. Its annual budget is $2.5 billion. It is true that approximately 75 percent of this is devoted to defense activities. Yet, some $600 million per year are also dedicated to peaceful arts—to the development of productive industries for the present and the future, such as power reactors and research on controlled fusion; to the advance of medicine and its application; to the growth of knowledge in many areas of fundamental research; to the export of materials and techniques as a part of our international relations program. In addition, there is the private atomic energy industry, involving nongovernmental expenditures of $50 million annually on development, and with a capital investment of $400 to $500 million. And we can hardly visualize the ultimate potential of this great private industry. Yet, all of this emanated from one discovery in basic research.

The new relationship between society and science is also reflected in the spectacular growth in the numbers of people who are engaged in research and development or who play supporting roles in these efforts. It is to be seen in the federal budget for research and development—some $9 billion annually today, as compared with about $400 million in 1940. Even more important are the new attitudes—of society in general toward science, and of scientists toward society.

The former is symbolized by the policies of government and industry. Recognition by the government of the need to support basic research across a broad spectrum was slow and spotty after World War II. The tendency has been— and continues to be to a large extent—to support fashionable or dramatic areas and those that might have some early, foreseeable technological value. Considerable progress was made, however, in the early postwar days as a result of the enlightened policies of the Office of Naval Research and the later policies of the Atomic Energy Commission. The National Science Foundation has significantly expanded the concept of governmental support for broad advances in fundamental knowledge, and I believe this trend will continue and will increasingly embrace the policies of special agencies that support research. Today, about 12 percent of the federal funds for research and development are used to support basic research fields. In other words, we can detect a fairly general recognition of the fact that the growth of fundamental knowledge, even though it may not have specific foreseeable application, contributes to the general welfare. Perhaps we can even hope for an appreciation of the more subtle cultural values of basic research.

The enormous impact of the past two decades on the

scientific community reflects significant integration of science into society. I do not detect any qualitative change in the spirit of scientific inquiry, fortunately. But it would appear that there is an important alteration in the attitude of scientists about the relationship of their work to the larger social environment. Many of us can recall a fairly general feeling of pride among scientists in the isolation of their work from the practical affairs of men. Indeed, it was not difficult to find resentment at any implication that a piece of research should have more than the remotest connection with application. Now, with the reduction of the time gap between basic and applied research, and with growing general appreciation of the value of knowledge, scientists seem more willing to relate themselves and their work to social objectives.

The material conditions have been modified, too. More and more, scientists find that they are supported adequately, if not opulently, and for sustained programs. Funds are available for "elegant" equipment that saves time and gives investigators greater power. Money can be obtained for assistants to do detailed work, giving researchers more time for creative effort. The improvements are not uniform, of course. Space to work is still in short supply, especially in our graduate schools, though new governmental policies promise some alleviation, and the personal rewards are still relatively less for those who train our scientists and generate much of our knowledge than for many others in our society who play much less significant roles.

The consolidation of science into society is striking in the field of governmental policy and international relations. The government has become increasingly dependent upon scientists for advice. This is true not only in the sphere of the administration of government science but in a much more comprehensive way. Any evaluation of the future of the economy must embrace scientific and technological knowledge. Decisions in military matters are intimately involved with science and technology. And any commitment of portions of our national resources for science and technology themselves must be decided with the help of men of wide knowledge in these fields.

The entry of scientists into areas where they serve the nation in important advisory capacities is an inevitable concomitant of the events of the last 20 years. I believe it is a healthy and essential development, and I have advocated it for many years. It does not seem to me that the influence of scientists in this respect is greater than it should be; indeed, in the national interest, I believe it must increase.

The question of the place of science in government touches upon some of the critical questions about the future evolution of a scientific society in a democratic context. Our aim must be to use science to strengthen democracy, not weaken it; to expand the potential fulfillment of the individual, not decrease it. We must avoid any erosion of the broad base of informed participation by the electorate. In the past two decades our democracy has ingested science, but it has not yet digested it—a measure of the infancy of our scientific society. This is not surprising, since our previous experience had not prepared us for anything like the explosion of those 20 years. We must expect the next 20 years to be even more dynamic. Therefore, it is urgent that we accelerate the process of assimilation.

A central problem in assimilation, it seems to me, is the extent to which men, including the otherwise well educated, fail to identify freedom of scientific inquiry with our political and other freedoms. In the somewhat less complicated world of the 18th century, a great thinker like Thomas Jefferson could be all at once a political theorist and practitioner, a philosopher, and a scientist. His mind could embrace and integrate a very large part of human knowledge. He had, therefore, a clear appreciation of the broadly humanistic values which are the common heritage of all men who pursue the truth.

But as knowledge grew and fragmented, the specialties went their separate ways. Science has seemed to walk more apart than other fields, perhaps because the details of scientific truth touch infrequently a community of intellectual experience. Science became a stranger even to many intellectuals.

This estrangement has resulted in the paradox with which we are familiar: as science became more important to society, it apparently became less important in the curricula of liberal education. This fact was noticed as long ago as the last century by Thomas Huxley, who pleaded with contemporaries holding a narrow view of humanism to include a more generous helping of science in liberal education. A cultured or liberally educated person, Huxley maintained, is one capable of making a criticism of life—of evaluating the environment and making enlightened judgments.

Thirty years ago George Sarton wrote in the same vein in his volume *The History of Science and the New Humanism*. He stated the issue, which remains central for our nascent democratic-scientific society, as follows:

> The main issue does not simply concern humanism but the whole of education from the cradle to the grave. And the real question is: will education include science, or will it exclude it? The intellectual elite is at present divided into two hostile groups—which we might call for short the literary and scientific—who do not speak the same language nor think in the same way. If nothing is done, the gap separating them must necessarily increase, together with the steady and irresistible progress of science. Shall we deliberately widen the gap as the old humanists would have it, or shall we take special pains to reduce it as much as we can?

In our time, G. P. Snow has eloquently drawn attention to the same problem, in his discourses on the "two cultures."

To summarize the matter, I should like to ask a question paraphrasing Huxley: Who in our times can make an adequate criticism of life without knowledge of the ideals, the methods, and the dynamics of science?

The remedies have been widely discussed: a larger content of science in the lower schools and in the universities and colleges; a wide range of efforts to give the public some appreciation of science; a greater effort by scientists to explain their work in popular terms.

All of these measures are needed. It is necessary to bring about a larger understanding of scientific principles. But in striving toward this goal it may be even more important to promote a greater consciousness of the common heritage of all who pursue the truth. The philosopher, the social scientist, the artist, the writer, the natural scientist—all are intellectual brothers under the skin. Whether their technique involves the distillation of human experience or the ordering of measurable phenomena into statements of principles, their motivations, the quality of their experiences, and their satisfactions are rooted in a broadly defined humanism.

I am sure intellectuals generally know this to be true. Yet it would appear that it is often far back in the consciousness. I wonder if this fact is not responsible for much of the inability of Snow's two cultures to communicate? I wonder if there is not a common language, deriving from a community of basic ideals and purposes, whatever the details of different bodies of knowledge, that is the foundation for communication? I wonder if the barriers are not superficial, even as language is a superficial obstacle between men who share common bonds?

The achievement of a conscious, working realization of the common heritage of truth-seekers—among scientists as well as other intellectuals—can be significant in the successful evolution of our new kind of society. It should make it clearer that the free and uninhibited pursuit of truth in science is a natural part of the right of free inquiry that is inherent in democracy. It should do much to abolish fruitless discussions over whether we should continue the pursuit of science and whether scientists should not withhold scientific truths that may be used destructively. It should give wider acceptance of the inevitable growth of knowledge and of its continual change. It should force us to a greater awareness of the need to prepare for and to cope with the hazards that are a paradoxical by-product of the expansion of knowledge.

It has seemed natural to lay some emphasis on science in

this discussion of the society that has developed in the last 20 years. I do not wish to give the impression, however, that I believe this new kind of society is the property of science. We cannot, of course, proceed intelligently without integrating into our thinking and our acting the full range of human wisdom. You will note that I have asked primarily for men generally, and for intellectuals in particular, to return science to the fold of humanism. It is unthinkable that a democratic-scientific society could evolve constructively without a wide endowment among its people of art, music, history, literature, and social dynamics.

We can hardly discuss the future of the scientific society without relating it to the world struggle and the terrible dilemma confronting man as the result of the development of nuclear weapons.

I am reminded of the reaction of many scientists, including some of us who worked on nuclear weapons, to this dilemma, when it became a reality in 1945. Natural scientists sometimes have been called too optimistic and naive by social scientists. As a group, they are not lacking in idealism. Perhaps it was natural that many of us, recognizing from close at hand the significance of nuclear weapons, set out to advise the world that nuclear war was out of the question. To us, the data were unequivocal, the conclusions indisputable, and the course of action clear. We felt the world would quickly see this—and, seeing it, do something about it.

The half-life of disillusionment varied from individual to individual. Few have changed their minds about nuclear war. But many have become more sophisticated, if less idealistic. Much of what has been described as naiveté has rubbed off. But we should remember that idealism, happily, has not been limited to scientists. In the period following World War I, experienced statesmen, imperceptibly influenced by scientists, solemnly signed unrealistic treaties outlawing war. Perhaps sophisticated statesmen, aided by sophisticated scientists in an age of science, may be able to combine realism and idealism.

My own instruction in these matters includes the experience, earlier this year, of being appointed by President Kennedy to head the U.S. delegation to the 5th Annual Conference of the International Atomic Energy Agency, in Vienna. This is an agency established to spread the peaceful uses of atomic energy throughout the world. Its problems, I found, are hardly less difficult than those of the United Nations.

I was impressed with the enormous difficulty of finding common solutions to problems when the effort had to be made with individuals who seem to speak a different language, not only linguistically but ideologically, and some of whom appear to possess a deterministic faith that is alien to our humanism.

While I found no basis for arrant optimism, neither did I find reason to stop trying. In the absence of any foreseeable breakthrough in diplomacy, it would appear that the best condition of the world we can hope for is a continuing crisis. In the competition of ideas which will accompany the crisis, the victory may be won by the successful evolution, here, of a society combining science and freedom.

Scientists and engineers can continue to make a major contribution in this contest, not only by achievements in the laboratory but also by participation in exchange programs and international meetings, and in other contacts with Iron Curtain nations through the medium of basic research, when and if the occasions arise. All these activities are essential to help keep the channels of communication and understanding open.

I believe each of us, scientist and nonscientist alike, must be aware of the importance of his own effort to the preservation of a libertarian society in the continuing crisis. Each of us needs a sense of responsibility and urgency for the total of our efforts will be decisive, however remote from combat our work may seem. We must not do too little. We cannot delay. We must have both determination and good intentions; and what is most important, *we must act*. As I have advocated in the past, we must expand and raise the level of education all along the line. We must, especially, search out and cultivate the gifted and creative, for it is these who usually make the great breakthroughs in knowledge and understanding. We must mine every vein of our human resources and exploit our talents in the fullest measure.

The democratic-scientific society has taken root in the past two decades, combining the values of freedom and individual worth with the promise of growing material well-being. Can we preserve it—not only for ourselves, but as a choice for other peoples?

I believe we can and will, partly because of the moral strength of freedom and partly because of the material power of our new society. We cannot be blind to the fact that freedom needs strength and determination as well as a good heart. Generosity has its place in relations between men, but it is, unfortunately, a quality not uniformly respected by all nations in relations between themselves. This is why, for example, we must be prepared to negotiate from a position of unquestioned strength as well as undoubted good faith. And negotiate we must; to turn our back on this most hopeful and sensible solution of the differences between East and West would be as foolish as it could perhaps be fatal. But we must recognize that until all nations can proceed from the same definition of right and truth, international agreements which involve our vital interests must incorporate provision for adequate controls against violations as well as provision recognizing the other's rights. We must be firm when our own security is at stake, as well as fair when another's is. I cannot help but recall, in this vein, that eloquent passage from President Kennedy's inaugural address: "civility is not a sign of weakness, and sincerity is always subject to proof. Let us never negotiate out of fear. But let us never fear to negotiate."

Beyond these principles, my confidence in freedom is based upon a personal faith, originating in my interpretation of human experience, to which one must appeal when scientific data are lacking or inconclusive. Many times in history the future has not looked bright. However, the things most feared have not always come to pass. Man's native faith and hope in his own destiny have motivated him to solve awesome problems. History does, we know, repeat itself— both in crises and in their resolution—and so, we must trust it will again.

Science, the study of natural law, can never be provincial, as Sinnott has pointed out. It is perhaps more truly international than any other form of human activity. When national considerations have entered into scientific activity, they have often resulted in error and confusion. The reverse is also true. No one nation is scientifically self-sufficient. Indeed there are scientific programs, such as the International Geophysical Year, or programs of astronomical observation, that would be impossible without international cooperation. It is a hopeful sign that nations politically at odds, such as Russia and the United States, have participated in such programs.

The author of the present article has reason to be interested in the subject. He is perhaps Germany's foremost living nuclear physicist. After studying in Munich, he became Max Born's assistant at Göttingen and later studied under Niels Bohr. He is a Nobel Prize winner and is best known for his statement of the "uncertainty principle," one of the landmarks in contemporary physics. During World War II, he was Director of the Max Planck Institute of Physics at Berlin. After hostilities ceased his future became the subject of an international dispute. His services were sought by all the conquering nations, but he decided to remain in his native country. As his article makes evident, he remains a true internationalist.

SCIENCE AS A MEANS OF INTERNATIONAL UNDERSTANDING

WERNER KARL HEISENBERG

IT HAS OFTEN BEEN SAID that science should be a bridge between peoples and should help to better international understanding. It has also repeatedly been stressed, with full justification, that science is international and that it directs man's thoughts to matters which are understood by all peoples and in whose solution scientists of the most diverse languages, races or religions can participate equally. At this particular time it is important that we should not make things too easy for ourselves. We must also discuss the opposite thesis, which is still fresh in our ears, that science is national and that the ideas of the various races are fundamentally different. It was held that science had to serve one's own people in the first instance and help to secure one's own political power: that science forms the basis of all technical developments, and hence of all progress, as well as of all military power. It was also held that the task of the pure sciences as well as of philosophy was to support our Weltanschauung and our beliefs. These in turn were regarded as the foundations of political power among our own people. I should like to discuss which of these two views is correct and what are the relative merits of the arguments that can be produced in their favor.

I

To gain clarity on this question we shall have to discover, in the first instance, how science is carried on, how an individual is brought into contact with scientific problems and how these problems excite his interest. Since I know only my own science well, you will not misunderstand me if I first

233

speak about atomic physics and if I recall my own experiences as a student.

When I left school in 1920 in order to attend at the University of Munich, the position of our youth as citizens was very similar to what it is today. Our defeat in the first world war had produced a deep mistrust of all the ideals which had been used during the war and which had lost us that war. They seemed hollow now and we wanted to find out for ourselves what was of value in this world and what was not: we did not want to rely on our parents or our teachers. Apart from many other values we re-discovered science in this process. After having studied a few popular books I began to take an interest in the branch of science concerned with atoms, and wanted to form an opinion of the peculiar statements which were being made about space and time in the theory of relativity. In this way I came to attend the lectures of my later teacher, Sommerfeld, who fanned this interest and from whom I learnt, in the course of the term, how a new and deeper understanding of atoms had developed as a result of the researches of Röntgen, Planck, Rutherford, and Bohr. I came to know that the Dane, Niels Bohr, and the Englishman, Lord Rutherford, imagined an atom to be a planetary system in miniature and that it was likely that all the chemical properties of the elements would, in future, be predictable with the help of Bohr's theory, by making use of the planetary orbits of the electrons. At that time, however, this had not been achieved. This last point naturally interested me most and every new work of Bohr was discussed at the Munich Seminar with vigor and passion. You can well imagine what it meant for me when Sommerfeld invited me, in the summer of 1921, to accompany him to Göttingen to hear a series of lectures given by Niels Bohr about his atomic theory. It was held in this very "Collegienhaus." This cycle of lectures in Göttingen, which in future was always to be referred to as the "Bohr Festival," has in many ways determined my future attitude to science and especially to atomic physics.

First of all, we could sense in Bohr's lectures the power of the ideas of a man who had seriously grappled with these problems and who understood them better than anyone else in the whole world. Secondly, there were some points on which I had previously formed an opinion different from that expounded by Bohr. These questions were fought out during long walks to the Rohn and to the Hainberg.

These conversations left a deep impression on me. First I learnt that when trying to understand atomic structure it was obviously quite immaterial whether one was German, Danish or English. I also learnt something perhaps even more important, namely that in science a decision can always be reached as to what is right and what is wrong. It was not a question of belief, or Weltanschauung, or hypothesis; but a certain statement could either be simply right and another statement simply wrong. Neither origin nor race decides this question: it is decided by nature, or if you prefer, by God, in any case not by man.

Very much enriched by these experiences, I returned to Munich and continued, under Sommerfeld's direction, with my own experiments on atomic structures. When I had completed my Doctor's examination I went to Copenhagen, in the autumn of 1924, with the aid of a so-called Rockefeller Grant, in order to work with Bohr. There I came into a circle of young people of the most diverse nationalities— English, American, Swedish, Norwegian, Dutch and Japanese—all of whom wanted to work on the same problem, Bohr's atomic theory. They nearly always joined together like a big family for excursions, games, social gatherings and sports. In this circle of physicists I had the opportunity of really getting to know people from other nations and their ways of thought. The learning and speaking of other languages which this necessitated was the best way of becoming really familiar with other ways of life, foreign literatures and foreign art. I could see more and more clearly how little mattered the diversity of nations and races when there was common effort centered on a difficult scientific problem. The differences of thought which were so clearly shown in art seemed to me more of an enrichment of one's own possibilities than a disturbing factor.

With this background I arrived in Cambridge in the summer of 1925, and spoke about my work to a small circle of theoreticians in a College, in the study of the Russian physicist Kapitza. Among those present, there was an unusually gifted student hardly twenty-three years old who took my problems and constructed, within a few months, a comprehensive theory of the atomic shell. His name was Dirac and he was a man of outstanding mathematical ability. His methods of thought were vastly different from mine, his mathematical methods more elegant and more unusual than those to which we were used at Göttingen. However, in the end, he arrived at the same results as Born, Jordan and I, at least on all points of importance. This confirmation and the fact that the results were so beautifully complementary served as further proof of the "objectivity" of science and its independence of language, race or belief.

As well as Copenhagen and Cambridge, Göttingen remained a center for this international family of atomic physicists. The work was directed by Franck. Born and Pohl and many of the scientists about whom you read in the newspapers in connection with the atom bomb, such as Oppenheimer and Blackett, as well as Fermi studied in Göttingen at that time.

I have quoted these personal reminiscences only in order to give an example of the internationalism of the community of science. It has, of course, been the same for centuries in many other sciences and this family of atomic physicists was in no way out of the ordinary. I could quote many international groups of "savants" from the history of science who were linked through the frontiers of nations by common work.

Perhaps I might mention one other group of scientists who, in the seventeenth century, founded mathematical science in Europe. It is especially appropriate to do so because the memory of Leibnitz is being celebrated this year as well as the foundation of the Scientific Academies. I should like to quote a few sentences of Dilthey's description of that epoch:

A bond, unhampered by any limitations of language or nationality, linked the few individuals who devoted their lives to this new science. They formed a new aristocracy and were conscious of it, just as before in the days of the Renaissance, humanists and artists had felt themselves to be such an aristocracy. The Latin and, later on, the French language rendered the easiest mutual understanding possible and they became the instrument of a scientific world literature. Already around the middle of the seventeenth century, Paris had become the center of collaboration between philosophers and scientists. There Gassendi, Marsenne and Hobbes exchanged ideas and even the proud recluse Descartes joined their circle for a time. His presence made an unforgettable impression on Hobbes and later Leibnitz; for it was there that both became devoted to the ideas of mathematical science. Later, London became another center . . . .[1]

We can see then that science has been carried on in this way throughout history and that the "Republic of Sages" has always played an important part in the life of Europe. It has always been considered self-evident that adherence to such an international circle would not prevent the individual scientist from devotedly serving his own people and feeling himself one of them. On the contrary, such a broadening of one's horizon frequently enhances esteem for the best aspects of the life of one's own country. One learns to love it and feels indebted to it.

II

Having said all this I must now also deal with the question of why all this scientific collaboration, all these real human relationships, seemingly do so little in preventing animosity and war.

First of all it must be stressed that science represents only a small part of public life and that only very few people in each country are really connected with science. Politics, however, are shaped by stronger forces. They have to take

1. Dilthey: Gesammelte Werke Bd. III, S 15, 16.

into account the actions of large masses of people, their economic position and the struggle for power of a few privileged groups favored by tradition. These forces have, so far, always overpowered the small number of people who were ready to discuss disputed questions in a scientific way —that is, objectively, dispassionately and in the spirit of mutual understanding. The political influence of science has always been very small, and this is understandable enough. It does, however, frequently place the scientist in a position which is in some ways more difficult than that of any other group of men. For science has, in its practical applications, a very great influence on the life of the people. Prosperity and political power depend on the state of science and the scientist cannot ignore these practical consequences even if his own interest in science is of a less practical nature. Thus, the action of an individual scientist often carries far more weight than he would wish and he frequently has to decide, according to his own conscience, whether a cause is good or bad. When the differences between nations can no longer be reconciled he is therefore often faced with the painful decision either of cutting himself off from his own people or from those friends who are linked with him by their common work. The position in the various sciences is here somewhat different. The medical practitioner, who helps people irrespective of their nationality, can more easily reconcile his actions to the demands of the state and of his own conscience than the physicist, whose discoveries may lead to the manufacture of weapons of destruction. But, by and large, there always remains this tension; there are on the one hand the demands of the state, which wants to enlist science particularly for the benefit of its own people and hence the strengthening of its own political power. On the other hand there is the duty owed by the scientist to his work which links him to people of other nations.

The relations between the scientist and the state have changed in a characteristic way during the past decades. During the first world war the scientists were so closely tied to their states that Academies frequently expelled scientists of other countries or signed resolutions in favor of their own cause and against the cause of the other nations. This hardly happened at all during the second world war. The link between the scientists was frequently much stronger, even to the extent, in many countries, of difficulties arising between them and their own governments. Scientists claimed the right to judge the policies of their governments independently and without ideological bias. The State, on its side, viewed the international relations of scientists with deep mistrust so that eventually scientists were sometimes even treated like prisoners in their own country and their international relations considered almost immoral. Conversely it has now become almost a matter of course that scientists will help their colleagues wherever possible, even though they belong to the enemy country. This development may lead to a fortunate strengthening of international, as against national, relations, but care will have to be taken that it does not become the origin of a dangerous wave of mistrust and enmity of large masses of people against the profession of science itself.

There have been such difficulties in previous centuries when men of science stood up for the principle of tolerance and independence from dogma against the current political power. We need only think of a Galileo or a Giordano Bruno. That these difficulties have assumed even greater importance today may be because the practical effects of science can directly decide the fate of millions of people.

This brings me to a frightening aspect of our present-day existence which has to be clearly recognized so that the correct action can be taken. I am not only thinking of the new sources of energy which physics has mastered during the last year and which could lead to unimaginable destruction. New possibilities of interfering with nature are threatening us in many other fields, though it is true that chemical means of destroying life have hardly been used in this last war. In biology, too, we have gained such insight into the processes of heredity and into the structure and chemistry of large albumen molecules that it has become a practical possibility to produce infectious diseases artificially, and perhaps worse, even the biological development of man may be influenced in the direction of some predetermined selective breeding. Finally, the mental and spiritual state of people could be influenced and, if this were carried out from a scientific point of view, it could lead to terrible mental deformations of great masses of people. One has the impression that science approaches on a broad front a region in which life and death of humanity at large can become dependent on the actions of a few, very small groups of people. Up to now these things have been discussed in a journalistic and sensational way in the newspapers and most people have not realized the terrible danger which threatens them as a result of further inevitable scientific developments. It is certainly the task of science to rouse humanity to these dangers and to show them how important it is that all mankind, independent of national and ideological views, should unite to meet the peril. Of course, this is more easily said than done, but it is certainly a task which we can no longer escape.

For the individual scientist there remains, however, the necessity of deciding according to his own conscience and free from all ties, whether a cause is good or even which of two causes is less bad. We cannot escape the fact that large masses of people, and with them those who hold the power of government, often act senselessly and with blind prejudice. By giving them the scientific knowledge the scientist can easily be maneuvered into a position which Schiller describes in these verses:

"Woe to those who bestow the light of heaven on him who is for ever blind, it sheds no light for him, it can but char and blacken lands and cities."

Can science really contribute to understanding between the peoples when it is faced with such a situation? It has the power to release great forces, greater than have ever before been in the control of man, but these forces will lead into chaos unless they are sensibly used.

III

This leads me to the real inherent task of science. The development which I have just described and which has apparently turned against himself those forces which man controls and which can lead to the most terrible destruction, this development must certainly be closely connected with some spiritual processes of our time, and it is necessary to speak briefly about these.

Let us look back a few centuries. At the end of the Middle Ages man discovered, apart from the Christian reality centered round the divine revelation, yet another reality of material experience. That was "objective" reality which we experience through our senses or by experiment. But in this advance into a new field certain methods of thought remained unchanged. Nature consisted of things in space which changed in time according to cause and effect. Outside of this there was the world of spirit, that is, the reality of one's own mind which reflected the external world like a more or less perfect mirror. Much as the reality determined by the sciences differed from the Christian reality, it nevertheless represented also a divine world order with man's action based on a firm foundation, and in which there could be little doubt about the purpose of life. The world was infinite in space and time, it had in a way replaced God or had at least become, by its infinity, a symbol of the divine.

But this view of nature has also become undermined during our century. Fundamental attitudes of thought lost their absolute importance as concrete action moved more and more into the center of our world. Even time and space became a subject of experience and lost their symbolic content. In science we realize more and more that our understanding of nature cannot begin with some definite cognition, that it cannot be built on such a rock-like foundation, but that all cognition is, so to speak, suspended over an unfathomable depth.

This development of science corresponds probably to the increasingly relative assessment of all values in the life of man, an assessment which has been noticeable for some decades and which can easily end up in a generally skeptical attitude capped by the desperate question "for what purpose." Thus develops the attitude of unbelief which we call "nihilism." From this point of view life appears to be purposeless or, at best, an adventure which we have to endure while having had no say in it. We find this attitude in many parts of the world today and its most unpleasant form is illusionary nihilism, as v. Weizsäcker recently called it. It is a nihilism disguised by illusion and self-deception.

The characteristic trait of every nihilist attitude is the lack of a solid belief which can give direction and strength to all the reactions of an individual. Nihilism shows itself in the life of an individual by his lack of an unerring instinct for right and wrong, for what is an illusion and what is a reality. In the life of nations it leads to a change of direction in which the immense forces, which have been gathered for the achievement of a certain aim, have the very opposite result and this can cause great destruction. People are often so blinded by hatred that they cynically watch this change and dispose of it with a shrug of the shoulder.

I said a little earlier that this development in the outlook of men may have some relation to the development of scientific thought. We must therefore ask whether science too has lost its solid beliefs. I am very anxious to make it quite clear that there can be no question of this. The very opposite is true. The present situation of science is probably the strongest argument we possess for a more optimistic attitude to the great problems of the world.

For in *those* branches of science in which we have found that our knowledge is "suspended in mid-air" in *just those* branches have we achieved a crystal clear understanding of the relevant phenomena. This knowledge is so transparent and carries such force of conviction that scientists of the most diverse peoples and races have accepted it as the undoubted basis of all further thought and cognition. Of course, we also make mistakes in science and it may take some time before these are found and corrected. But we can rest assured that there will be a final decision as to what is right and what is wrong. This decision will not depend on the belief, race or origin of the scientists, but it will be taken by a higher power and will then apply to all men for all time. While we cannot avoid in political life a constant change of values, a struggle of one set of illusions and misleading ideas against another set of illusions and equally misleading ideas, there will always be a "right or wrong" in science. There is a higher power, not influenced by our wishes, which finally decides and judges. The core of science is formed, to my mind, by the pure sciences, which are not concerned with practical applications. They are the branches in which pure thought attempts to discover the hidden harmonies of nature. Mankind today may find this innermost circle in which science and art can hardly be separated, in which the personification of pure truth is no longer disguised by human ideologies and desires.

You may, of course, object that the great mass of people has no access to this truth and that it can therefore exert little influence on the attitude of people. But at no time did the great mass of people have direct access to the center and it may be that people today will be satisfied to know that though the gate is not open to everyone there *can* be no deceit beyond the gate. We have no power there—the decisions are taken by a higher power. People have used different words at different times for this "center." They called it "spirit" or "God," or they spoke in similes, or in terms of sound or picture. There are many ways to this center, even today, and science is only one of them. Perhaps we have no longer a generally recognized language in which we can make ourselves intelligible. That may be the reason why so many people cannot see it, but it is there today as it has always been, and any world order must be based on it. Such a world order must be guided by men who have not lost sight of it.

Science can contribute to the understanding between peoples. It can do so not because it can render succor to the sick, nor because of the terror which some political power may wield with its aid, but only by turning our attention to that "center" which can establish order in the world at large, perhaps simply to the fact that the world is beautiful. It may appear presumptuous to attribute such importance to science but may I remind you that though we have cause to envy previous epochs in many aspects of life, our age is second to none in scientific achievement, in the pure cognition of nature.

Whatever may happen, interest in knowledge itself will remain a potent force in mankind for the next few decades. Even though this interest may for some time be overshadowed by the practical consequences of science and by the struggle for power it must eventually triumph and link together people of all nations and races. In all parts of the world people will be happy when they have gained new knowledge and they will be grateful to the man who first discovered it.

Saint Augustine, born in 354, was not dogmatic about the sphericity of the earth but rejected the idea that men existed on the other side because "Scripture speaks of no such descendants of Adam." In the eighth century, Saint Boniface denied the existence of the Antipodes on the ground that it amounted to "a declaration that there were men on the earth beyond the reach of salvation." These quotations are taken from a small book published in 1876 by Andrew D. White, President of Cornell, entitled The Warfare of Science. It was later expanded into a larger work entitled A History of the Warfare of Science with Theology in Christendom (1896), which attained great popularity and is still in active circulation. In the first book White stated, "In all modern history, interference with science in the supposed interest of religion, no matter how conscientious such interference may have been, has resulted in the direst evils to both religion and to science—and invariably. And, on the other hand, all untrammeled scientific investigation, no matter how dangerous to religion some of its stages may have seemed, for the time, to be, has invariably resulted in the highest good of religion and of science. I say

'invariably.' I mean exactly that. It is a rule to which history
shows not one exception."

His argument can be buttressed by innumerable examples,
among them the imprisonment of Galileo, the martyrdom of
Bruno, the attacks on Darwin, and more recently, such affairs
as the Scopes trial in 1925.

Many millions of words have of course been written on every
conceivable aspect of the problem. In his statement quoted
above, White offers hope that it can perhaps be resolved. This
is also the viewpoint of Alfred North Whitehead in "Religion
and Science," which has been included because it presents
an unusual aspect of the subject, because it invokes neither
sect nor dogma, and because it is written by one of the most
distinguished philosophers and scientific thinkers of the twen-
tieth century. Whitehead was born at Ramsgate, England,
in 1861 and died at Cambridge, Massachusetts, in 1947. He
was a lecturer in mathematics at Cambridge and a professor at
the University of London. In 1924, he joined the faculty at
Harvard, where he formulated an abstruse and difficult idealistic
philosophy based on mathematical concepts. He is best known
for his Principia Mathematica, which he wrote with Bertrand
Russell, and for his other books on mathematics, as well as
for Science in the Modern World, from which this selection
is taken.

RELIGION AND SCIENCE

ALFRED NORTH WHITEHEAD

THE DIFFICULTY IN APPROACHING the question of the relations between Religion and Science is, that its elucidation
requires that we have in our minds some clear idea of what
we mean by either of the terms, 'religion' and 'science.' Also
I wish to speak in the most general way possible, and to
keep in the background any comparison of particular creeds,

scientific or religious. We have got to understand the type of connection which exists between the two spheres, and then to draw some definite conclusions respecting the existing situation which at present confronts the world.

The *conflict* between religion and science is what natural-ly occurs to our minds when we think of this subject. It seems as though, during the last half-century, the results of science and the beliefs of religion had come into a position of frank disagreement, from which there can be no escape, except by abandoning either the clear teaching of science, or the clear teaching of religion. This conclusion has been urged by controversialists on either side. Not by all con-troversialists, of course, but by those trenchant intellects which every controversy calls out into the open.

The distress of sensitive minds, and the zeal for truth, and the sense of the importance of the issues, must com-mand our sincerest sympathy. When we consider what re-ligion is for mankind, and what science is, it is no exaggera-tion to say that the future course of history depends upon the decision of this generation as to the relations between them. We have here the two strongest general forces (apart from the mere impulse of the various senses) which influ-ence men, and they seem to be set one against the other— the force of our religious intuitions, and the force of our impulse to accurate observation and logical deduction.

A great English statesman once advised his countrymen to use large-scale maps, as a preservative against alarms, panics, and general misunderstanding of the true relations between nations. In the same way in dealing with the clash between permanent elements of human nature, it is well to map our history on a large scale, and to disengage ourselves from our immediate absorption in the present conflicts. When we do this, we immediately discover two great facts. In the first place, there has always been a conflict between religion and science; and in the second place, both religion and science have always been in a state of continual development. In the early days of Christianity, there was a general belief among Christians that the world was coming to an end in the lifetime of people then living. We can make only indirect inferences as to how far this belief was authoritatively proclaimed; but it is certain that it was widely held, and that it formed an impressive part of the popular religious doctrine. The belief proved itself to be mistaken, and Christian doctrine adjusted itself to the change. Again in the early Church individual theologians very confidently deduced from the Bible opinions concerning the nature of the physical universe. In the year A.D. 535, a monk named Cosmas[1] wrote a book which he entitled, *Christian Topography*. He was a travelled man who had visited India and Ethiopia; and finally he lived in a monastery at Alexandria, which was then a great center of culture. In this book, basing himself upon the direct meaning of Biblical texts as construed by him in a literal fashion, he denied the existence of the antipodes, and asserted that the world is a flat parallelogram whose length is double its breadth.

In the seventeenth century the doctrine of the motion of the earth was condemned by a Catholic tribunal. A hundred years ago the extension of time demanded by geological science distressed religious people, Protestant and Catholic. And today the doctrine of evolution is an equal stumbling-block. These are only a few instances illustrating a general fact.

But all our ideas will be in a wrong perspective if we think that this recurring perplexity was confined to contradictions between religion and science; and that in these controversies religion was always wrong, and that science was always right. The true facts of the case are very much more complex, and refuse to be summarized in these simple terms.

Theology itself exhibits exactly the same character of gradual development, arising from an aspect of conflict between its own proper ideas. This fact is a commonplace to theologians, but is often obscured in the stress of controversy. I do not wish to overstate my case; so I will confine myself to Roman Catholic writers. In the seventeenth century a learned Jesuit, Father Petavius, showed that the

1. *Cf.* Lecky's *The Rise and Influence of Rationalism in Europe,* Ch. III.

theologians of the first three centuries of Christianity made use of phrases and statements which since the fifth century would be condemned as heretical. Also Cardinal Newman devoted a treatise to the discussion of the development of doctrine. He wrote it before he became a great Roman Catholic ecclesiastic; but throughout his life, it was never retracted and continually reissued.

Science is even more changeable than theology. No man of science could subscribe without qualification to Galileo's beliefs, or to Newton's beliefs, or to all his own scientific beliefs of ten years ago.

In both regions of thought, additions, distinctions, and modifications have been introduced. So that now, even when the same assertion is made today as was made a thousand, or fifteen hundred years ago, it is made subject to limitations or expansions of meaning, which were not contemplated at the earlier epoch. We are told by logicians that a proposition must be either true or false, and that there is no middle term. But in practice, we may know that a proposition expresses an important truth, but that it is subject to limitations and qualifications which at present remain undiscovered. It is a general feature of our knowledge, that we are insistently aware of important truth; and yet that the only formulations of these truths which we are able to make presuppose a general standpoint of conceptions which may have to be modified. I will give you two illustrations, both from science: Galileo said that the earth moves and that the sun is fixed; the Inquisition said that the earth is fixed and the sun moves; and Newtonian astronomers, adopting an absolute theory of space, said that both the sun and the earth move. But now we say that any one of these three statements is equally true, provided that you have fixed your sense of 'rest' and 'motion' in the way required by the statement adopted. At the date of Galileo's controversy with the Inquisition, Galileo's way of stating the facts was, beyond question, the fruitful procedure for the sake of scientific research. But in itself it was not more true than the formulation of the Inquisition. But at that time the modern concepts of relative motion were in nobody's mind; so that the

statements were made in ignorance of the qualifications required for their more perfect truth. Yet this question of the
motions of the earth and the sun expresses a real fact in the
universe; and all sides had got hold of important truths
concerning it. But with the knowledge of those times, the
truths appeared to be inconsistent.

Again I will give you another example taken from the state
of modern physical science. Since the time of Newton and
Huyghens in the seventeenth century there have been two
theories as to the physical nature of light. Newton's theory
was that a beam of light consists of a stream of very minute
particles, or corpuscles, and that we have the sensation of
light when these corpuscles strike the retinas of our eyes.
Huyghens' theory was that light consists of very minute
waves of trembling in an all-pervading ether, and that these
waves are travelling along a beam of light. The two theories
are contradictory. In the eighteenth century Newton's theory
was believed, in the nineteenth century Huyghens' theory
was believed. Today there is one large group of phenomena
which can be explained only on the wave theory, and another large group which can be explained only on the corpuscular theory. Scientists have to leave it at that, and wait
for the future, in the hope of attaining some wider vision
which reconciles both.

We should apply these same principles to the questions in
which there is a variance between science and religion. We
would believe nothing in either sphere of thought which
does not appear to us to be certified by solid reasons based
upon the critical research either of ourselves or of competent
authorities. But granting that we have honestly taken this
precaution, a clash between the two on points of detail
where they overlap should not lead us hastily to abandon
doctrines for which we have solid evidence. It may be that
we are more interested in one set of doctrines than in the
other. But, if we have any sense of perspective and of the
history of thought, we shall wait and refrain from mutual
anathemas.

We should wait: but we should not wait passively, or in
despair. The clash is a sign that there are wider truths and

finer perspectives within which a reconciliation of a deeper religion and a more subtle science will be found.

In one sense, therefore, the conflict between science and religion is a slight matter which has been unduly emphasized. A mere logical contradiction cannot in itself point to more than the necessity of some readjustments, possibly of a very minor character on both sides. Remember the widely different aspects of events which are dealt with in science and in religion respectively. Science is concerned with the general conditions which are observed to regulate physical phenomena; whereas religion is wholly wrapped up in the contemplation of moral and aesthetic values. On the one side there is the law of gravitation, and on the other the contemplation of the beauty of holiness. What one side sees, the other misses; and vice versa.

Consider, for example the lives of John Wesley and of Saint Francis of Assisi. For physical science you have in these lives merely ordinary examples of the operation of the principles of physiological chemistry, and of the dynamics of nervous reactions: for religion you have lives of the most profound significance in the history of the world. Can you be surprised that, in the absence of a perfect and complete phrasing of the principles of science and of the principles of religion which apply to these specific cases, the accounts of these lives from these divergent standpoints should involve discrepancies? It would be a miracle if it were not so.

It would however, be missing the point to think that we need not trouble ourselves about the conflict between science and religion. In an intellectual age there can be no active interest which puts aside all hope of a vision of the harmony of truth. To acquiesce in discrepancy is destructive of candor, and of moral cleanliness. It belongs to the self-respect of intellect to pursue every tangle of thought to its final unravelment. If you check that·impulse, you will get no religion and no science from an awakened thoughtfulness. The important question is, In what spirit are we going to face the issue? There we come to something absolutely vital.

A clash of doctrines is not a disaster—it is an opportunity. I will explain my meaning by some illustrations from science.

The weight of an atom of nitrogen was well known. Also it was an established scientific doctrine that the average weight of such atoms in any considerable mass will be always the same. Two experimenters, the late Lord Rayleigh and the late Sir William Ramsay, found that if they obtained nitrogen by two different methods, each equally effective for that purpose, they always observed a persistent slight difference between the average weights of the atoms in the two cases. Now I ask you, would it have been rational of these men to have despaired because of this conflict between chemical theory and scientific observation? Suppose that for some reason the chemical doctrine had been highly prized throughout some district as the foundation of its social order:—would it have been wise, would it have been candid, would it have been moral, to forbid the disclosure of the fact that the experiments produced discordant results? Or, on the other hand, should Sir William Ramsay and Lord Rayleigh have proclaimed that chemical theory was now a detected delusion? We see at once that either of these ways would have been a method of facing the issue in an entirely wrong spirit. What Rayleigh and Ramsay did was this: They at once perceived that they had hit upon a line of investigation which would disclose some subtlety of chemical theory that had hitherto eluded observation. The discrepancy was not a disaster: it was an opportunity to increase the sweep of chemical knowledge. You all know the end of the story: finally argon was discovered, a new chemical element which had lurked undetected, mixed with the nitrogen. But the story has a sequel which forms my second illustration. This discovery drew attention to the importance of observing accurately minute differences in chemical substances as obtained by different methods. Further researches of the most careful accuracy were undertaken. Finally another physicist, F. W. Aston, working in the Cavendish Laboratory at Cambridge in England, discovered that even the same element might assume two or more distinct forms, termed *isotopes*, and that the law of the constancy of average atomic weight holds for each of these forms, but as between the different isotopes differs slightly. The research has effected a great stride in the power of chemical theory, far transcending in importance the discovery of argon from which it originated. The moral of these stories lies on the surface, and I will leave to you their application to the case of religion and science.

In formal logic, a contradiction is the signal of a defeat: but in the evolution of real knowledge it marks the first step in progress towards a victory. This is one great reason for the utmost toleration of variety of opinion. Once and forever, this duty of toleration has been summed up in the words, 'Let both grow together until the harvest.' The failure of Christians to act up to this precept, of the highest authority, is one of the curiosities of religious history. But we have not yet exhausted the discussion of the moral temper required for the pursuit of truth. There are short cuts leading merely to an illusory success. It is easy enough to find a theory, logically harmonious and with important applications in the region of fact, provided that you are content to disregard half your evidence. Every age produces people with clear logical intellects, and with the most praiseworthy grasp of the importance of some sphere of human experience, who have elaborated, or inherited a scheme of thought which exactly fits those experiences which claim their interest. Such people are apt resolutely to ignore, or to explain away, all evidence which confuses their scheme with contradictory instances. What they cannot fit in is for them nonsense. An unflinching determination to take the whole evidence into account is the only method of preservation against the fluctuating extremes of fashionable opinion. This advice seems so easy, and is in fact so difficult to follow.

One reason for this difficulty is that we cannot think first and act afterwards. From the moment of birth we are immersed in action, and can only fitfully guide it by taking thought. We have, therefore, in various spheres of experience to adopt those ideas which seem to work within those spheres. It is absolutely necessary to trust to ideas which are generally adequate, even though we know that there are subtleties and distinctions beyond our ken. Also apart from the necessities of action, we cannot even keep before our minds the whole evidence except under the guise of doctrines which are incompletely harmonised. We cannot think in terms of an indefinite multiplicity of detail; our evidence can acquire its proper importance only if it comes before us marshalled by general ideas. These ideas we inherit—they form the tradition of our civilisation. Such traditional ideas are never static. They are either fading into meaningless formulae, or are gaining power by the new lights thrown by a more delicate apprehension. They are transformed by the urge of critical reason, by the vivid evidence of emotional experience, and by the cold certainties of scientific perception. One fact is certain, you cannot keep them still. No generation can merely reproduce its ancestors. You may preserve the life in a flux of form, or preserve the form amid an ebb of life, but you cannot permanently enclose the same life in the same mold.

The present state of religion among the European races illustrates the statements which I have been making. The phenomena are mixed. There have been reactions and revivals. But on the whole, during many generations there has been a gradual decay of religious influence in European civilisation. Each revival touches a lower peak than its predecessor, and each period of slackness a lower depth. The average curve marks a steady fall in religious tone. In some countries the interest in religion is higher than in others. But in those countries where the interest is relatively high, it still falls as the generations pass. Religion is tending to degenerate into a decent formula wherewith to embellish a comfortable life. A great historical movement on this scale results from the convergence of many causes. I wish to suggest two of them which lie within the scope of this chapter for consideration.

In the first place for over two centuries religion has been on the defensive and on a weak defensive. The period has been one of unprecedented intellectual progress. In this way a series of novel situations have been produced for thought. Each such occasion has found the religious thinkers unprepared. Something, which has been proclaimed to be vital, has finally, after struggle, distress, and anathema, been modified and otherwise interpreted. The next generation of religious apologists then congratulates the religious world on the deeper insight which has been gained. The result of the continued repetition of this undignified retreat, during many generations, has at last almost entirely destroyed the intellectual authority of religious thinkers. Consider this contrast: when Darwin or Einstein proclaims theories which modify our ideas, it is a triumph for science. We do not go about saying that there is another defeat for science, because its old ideas have been abandoned. We know that another step of scientific insight has been gained.

Religion will not regain its old power until it can face change in the same spirit as does science. Its principles may be eternal, but the expression of those principles requires continual development. This evolution of religion is in the main a disengagement of its own proper ideas from the adventitious notions which have crept into it by reason of the expression of its own ideas in terms of the imaginative picture of the world entertained in previous ages. Such a release of religion from the bonds of imperfect science is all to the good. It stresses its own genuine message. The great point to be kept in mind is that normally an advance in science will show that statements of various religious beliefs require some sort of modification. It may be that they have to be expanded or explained, or indeed entirely restated. If the religion is a sound expression of truth, this modification will only exhibit more adequately the exact point which is of importance. This process is a gain. In so far, therefore, as any religion has any contact with physical facts, it is to be expected that the point of view of those facts must be continually modified as scientific knowledge advances. In this way, the exact relevance of these facts for religious thought will grow more and more clear. The progress of science must result in the unceasing codification of religious thought, to the great advantage of religion.

The religious controversies of the sixteenth and seventeenth centuries put theologians into a most unfortunate state of mind. They were always attacking and defending. They pictured themselves as the garrison of a fort surrounded by hostile forces. All such pictures express half-truths. That is why they are so popular. But they are dangerous. This particular picture fostered a pugnacious party spirit which really expresses an ultimate lack of faith. They dared not modify, because they shirked the task of disengaging their spiritual message from the associations of a particular imagery.

Let me explain myself by an example. In the early medieval times, Heaven was in the sky, and Hell was underground; volcanoes were the jaws of Hell. I do not assert that these beliefs entered into the official formulations; but they did enter into the popular understanding of the general doctrines of Heaven and Hell. These notions were what everyone thought to be implied by the doctrine of the future state. They entered into the explanations of the influential exponents of Christian belief. For example, they occur in the *Dialogues* of Pope Gregory,[2] the Great, a man whose high official position is surpassed only by the magnitude of his services to humanity. I am not saying what we ought to believe about the future state. But whatever be the right doctrine, in this instance the clash between religion and science, which has relegated the earth to the position of a second-rate planet attached to a second-rate sun, has been greatly to the benefit of the spirituality of religion by dispersing these medieval fancies.

Another way of looking at this question of the evolution of religious thought is to note that any verbal form of statement which has been before the world for some time discloses ambiguities; and that often such ambiguities strike at the very heart of the meaning. The effective sense in which a doctrine has been held in the past cannot be determined by the mere logical analysis of verbal statements, made in ignorance of the logical trap. You have to take into account the whole reaction of human nature to the scheme of thought. This reaction is of a mixed character, including elements of emotion derived from our lower natures. It is here that the impersonal criticism of science and of philosophy comes to the aid of religious evolution. Example after example can be given of this motive force in development.

2. *Cf.* Gregorovius' *History of Rome in the Middle Ages,* Book III, Ch. III, Vol. II, English trans.

For example, the logical difficulties inherent in the doctrine of the moral cleansing of human nature by the power of religion rent Christianity in the days of Pelagius and Augustine —that is to say, at the beginning of the fifth century. Echoes of that controversy still linger in theology.

So far, my point has been this: that religion is the expression of one type of fundamental experiences of mankind: that religious thought develops into an increasing accuracy of expression, disengaged from adventitious imagery: that the interaction between religion and science is one great factor in promoting this development.

I now come to my second reason for the modern fading of interest in religion. This involves the ultimate question which I stated in my opening sentences. We have to know what we mean by religion. The churches, in their presentation of their answers to this query, have put forward aspects of religion which are expressed in terms either suited to the emotional reactions of bygone times or directed to excite modern emotional interests of nonreligious character. What I mean under the first heading is that religious appeal is directed partly to excite that instinctive fear of the wrath of a tyrant which was inbred in the unhappy populations of the arbitrary empires of the ancient world, and in particular to excite that fear of an all-powerful arbitrary tyrant behind the unknown forces of nature. This appeal to the ready instinct of brute fear is losing its force. It lacks any directness of response, because modern science and modern conditions of life have taught us to meet occasions of apprehension by a critical analysis of their causes and conditions. Religion is the reaction of human nature to its search for God. The presentation of God under the aspect of power awakens every modern instinct of critical reaction. This is fatal; for religion collapses unless its main positions command immediacy of assent. In this respect the old phraseology is at variance with the psychology of modern civilisations. This change in psychology is largely due to science, and is one of the chief ways in which the advance of science has weakened the hold of the old religious forms of expression. The nonreligious motive which has entered into modern religious thought is the desire for a comfortable organisation of modern society. Religion has been presented as valuable for the ordering of life. Its claims have been rested upon its function as a sanction to right conduct. Also the purpose of right conduct quickly degenerates into the formation of pleasing social relations. We have here a subtle degradation of religious ideas, following upon their gradual purification under the influence of keener ethical intuitions. Conduct is a by-product of religion—an inevitable by-product, but not the main point. Every great religious teacher has revolted against the presentation of religion as a mere sanction of rules of conduct. Saint Paul denounced the Law, and Puritan divines spoke of the filthy rags of righteousness. The insistence upon rules of conduct marks the ebb of religious fervor. Above and beyond all things, the religious life is not a research after comfort. I must now state, in all diffidence, what I conceive to be the essential character of the religious spirit.

Religion is the vision of something which stands beyond, behind, and within, the passing flux of immediate things; something which is real, and yet waiting to be realised; something which is a remote possibility, and yet the greatest of present facts; something that gives meaning to all that passes, and yet eludes apprehension; something whose possession is the final good, and yet is beyond all reach; something which is the ultimate ideal, and the hopeless quest.

The immediate reaction of human nature to the religious vision is worship. Religion has emerged into human experience mixed with the crudest fancies of barbaric imagination. Gradually, slowly, steadily the vision recurs in history under nobler form and with clearer expression. It is the one element in human experience which persistently shows an upward trend. It fades and then recurs. But when it renews its force, it recurs with an added richness and purity of content. The fact of the religious vision, and its history of persistent expansion, is our one ground for optimism. Apart from it, human life is a flash of occasional enjoyments lighting up a mass of pain and misery, a bagatelle of transient experience.

The vision claims nothing but worship; and worship is a surrender to the claim for assimilation, urged with the motive force of mutual love. The vision never overrules. It is always there, and it has the power of love presenting the one purpose whose fulfilment is eternal harmony. Such order as we find in nature is never force—it presents itself as the one harmonious adjustment of complex detail. Evil is the brute motive force of fragmentary purpose, disregarding the eternal vision. Evil is overruling, retarding, hurting. The power of God is the worship He inspires. That religion is strong which in its ritual and its modes of thought evokes an apprehension of the commanding vision. The worship of God is not a rule of safety—it is an adventure of the spirit, a flight after the unattainable. The death of religion comes with the repression of the high hope of adventure.